Foundations
Book 1

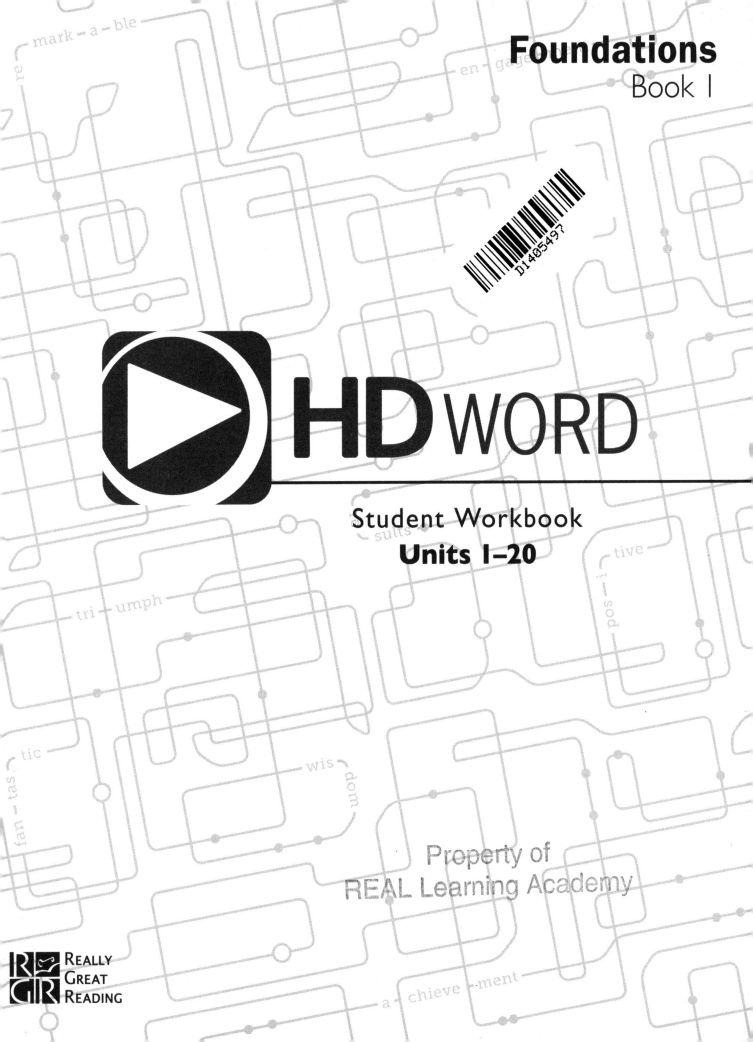

HD WORD

Student Workbook
Units 1–20

REALLY
GREAT
READING

Really Great Reading

PO Box 46
Cabin John, MD 20818
1-942598-18-1

www.ReallyGreatReading.com

Curriculum Development Team:
Janeen Hergert, M. Ed., Amy E. Vanden Boogart, M. Ed., Dara Wagner, M. Ed., Claudia Martín, MST

Graphic Design:
Ingrid Shwaiko, Nichole Monaghan

First Edition
978-1-942598-18-3
1942598181 AGS1115

Printed in the U.S.A.

▶ Table of Contents

Mark It!

1. <u>c h o p</u>
2. t h i n
3. s o c k
4. w i s h
5. f a l l
6. s h u t

7. p a c k
8. c h i c k
9. b a t h
10. w a l l
11. r u s h
12. w h a m

Read It!

1	chop	wish	pack
2	wall	thin	fall
3	chick	rush	sock
4	shut	bath	wham
5	wish	fall	chick
6	pack	sock	bath
7	rush	wall	shut
8	thin	wham	chop

Word Sort

If there is a digraph, underline both letters in the digraph together. Place a checkmark in the appropriate column, and circle the correct number of phonemes.

CHALLENGING

	Digraph	No Digraph	How many phonemes?			
1. lu<u>ck</u>	✓		1	2	③	4
2. fish			1	2	3	4
3. math			1	2	3	4
4. win			1	2	3	4

MORE CHALLENGING

	Digraph	No Digraph	How many phonemes?			
5. ash			1	2	3	4
6. back			1	2	3	4
7. mop			1	2	3	4
8. tick			1	2	3	4

MOST CHALLENGING

	Digraph	No Digraph	How many phonemes?			
9. which			1	2	3	4
10. cut			1	2	3	4
11. Phil			1	2	3	4
12. thick			1	2	3	4

CHALLENGING

1. the thin mesh net (4)
2. red sash had a big rip (6)
3. get a shot from the vet (6)
4. a big dish of thick mush (6)

MORE CHALLENGING

5. nick the rim of the dish (6)
6. did pick the fat tick off Chuck (7)
7. must get rid of the lock on the shed (9)
8. red chick was quick to peck the sack (8)

CHALLENGING

1. Sick Phil went to the doc for a quick fix. (10)
2. She shot the puck back in the net to win. (10)
3. I think that thud came from the back of the shop. (11)
4. Pick the rock out of the mud and set it back in the van. (14)

MORE CHALLENGING

5. When my sis was sick, she did not want to get a shot. (13)
6. When can we jog up to the dock at the back of the path? (14)
7. Rick saw the thick shell and gave the nut a big whack with a rock. (15)
8. The thug did not pick the lock, so the cop had to check the back of the shop. (18)

WORDS

1. Read each word.
2. <u>Underline</u> each digraph in the words below with one line. Some words may have more than one digraph.
3. Draw a box around the *chunk* **all** in the words below.
4. Circle all the words that rhyme with the word **sick**.

math	quick	tall	thud
thick	shut	when	much
chill	mall	fish	kick
check	lock	gush	shin
hall	shack	Phil	chop

Write six different digraphs you found in the words above.

___ ___ ___ ___ ___ ___

Choose **<u>two</u>** words from above, and write **<u>one</u>** sentence that includes both of those words on the lines below.

_____

_____

> Sample Sentence: **Six big fish swam in the river.**

1. Misread word - Draw a line through the word.

Reader: Six <u>black</u> fish swam in the river.

Marking: Six ~~big~~ fish swam in the river.

2. Word left out - Draw a line through the word.

Reader: Six fish swam in the river.

Marking: Six ~~big~~ fish swam in the river.

3. Word added - Draw an arrow (∨) where a word is added.

Reader: Six big fish swam in the <u>cold</u> river.

Marking: Six big fish swam in the∨river.

4. Skipped line - Cross off any line that is skipped.

The Reader skips the second line below.

The 16 words in the skipped line are counted as errors.

Sarah and her dad went fishing in the Trammer River. They were very excited.	14
~~Six big fish swam in the river. They were salmon on their way to the place~~	30
where they had been laid as eggs.	37

5. Self-correction - Write **SC** above the word with a line through the word.

Reader: Six fish, big fish, swam in the river.

Marking: Six ~~big~~ fish swam in the river. (SC above "big")

Self-corrections do not count as errors.

6. Last Word - Put a bracket (**]**) after the last word read.

The Reader's last word at the end of a minute was **had.**

Sarah and her dad went fishing in the Trammer River. They were very excited.	14
Six big fish swam in the river. They were salmon on their way to the place	30
where they had] been laid as eggs.	37

Errors

Misread word	six ~~big~~ fish
Word left out	six ~~big~~ fish
Word added	in the ⌄river
Skipped line	~~Six big fish swam in~~

Others

Self-correction	SC six ~~big~~ fish
Last word	they had]been

Practice Marking Errors with Sentences and Paragraphs

Practice Sentences:

1. Rob's new car was blue.

2. An eagle's nest can weigh up to 40 pounds.

3. Fish live in the fresh water of lakes, streams, rivers, and ponds.

4. Fish use fins and tails to move through the water.

5. Some kinds of fish swim in groups called schools.

Practice Paragraph:

Most fish lay eggs in nests around rocks or plants. Others just lay their eggs in the water. Some fish lay very large numbers of eggs, but not all the eggs will hatch. Predators will eat some of them. Others will not hatch because the water is too cold.

Practice Passage:

Think about a shark. If you are like most people, sharp teeth and scary attacks come to mind. However, only a few of the more than 300 types of sharks harm people. Sharks are fish, so they must live in water. Sharks mostly live in the salt water of the oceans. A few kinds of sharks can spend a short amount of time in fresh water. A few rare sharks live in fresh water full time.

Practice Tracking Chart

Date	9/18	9/21									
Reader 1	✓										
Reader 2		✓									
Reader 3											
Accuracy % Goal: 98% or better	92 %	95 %	%	%	%	%	%	%	%	%	%
100%											
99%											
98%											
97%											
96%											
95%		■									
94%		■									
93%		■									
92%	■	■									
91%	■	■									
90% or below	■	■									
Words Correct per Minute (WCPM)	65	61									
140 or above											
135–139											
130–134											
125–129											
120–124											
115–119											
110–114											
105–109											
100–104											
95–99											
90–94											
85–89											
80–84											
75–79											
70–74											
65–69	■	■									
60–64	■	■									
55–59	■	■									
50–54	■	■									
45–49	■	■									
below 40	■	■									

WAY TO GO!

98% or better PERCENTAGE   ACCURACY

Reader 1: _____   Date: _____

Reader 2: _____

Reader 3: _____

Words to Preview	Point & Say
1 **oxygen** – a colorless, odorless gas that is part of the air we breathe in. *People and animals need* **oxygen** *to live.*	breathe
	exercise
2 **carbon dioxide** – a colorless, odorless gas that is part of the air we breathe out. *People and animals breathe out* **carbon dioxide.**	hiccups
	fragile

Note: Hyphenated words count as one word.

The Lungs

READER 1

We use our lungs to breathe. When we breathe, our body gets the oxygen   14
it needs to stay alive. We breathe in and out through our nose and mouth.   29
Then the air makes its way to our lungs. The lungs breathe in oxygen and   44
breathe out carbon dioxide.   48

Our lungs are in our chests, near our hearts. They fill up most of the space   64
in our chests. They are pink and squishy. Our lungs are fragile, but   77
very important.   79

READER 2

We have two lungs, one on each side. The left lung is a bit smaller than the   96
right lung. The smaller lung makes room for the heart, which is on the left   111
side of our chests. Our hard rib cage wraps around our lungs and keeps   125
them safe.   127

When we breathe in, our lungs fill with air, like balloons, and our chests   141
get bigger. When we breathe out, our lungs empty. As the air leaves our   155
lungs, our chests get smaller.   160

We breathe in and out all the time without having to think about it. If we   176
try to hold our breath for a long time, our brain will make us start breathing   192
again soon.   194

READER 3

People breathe in and out about twenty times a minute. If we run fast,   208
our lungs need more oxygen so we breathe faster—about eighty times a   221
minute. The heart and the lungs work together. The heart pumps blood to   234
the lungs, and the lungs put oxygen in the blood. Then the heart sends this   249
oxygen-filled blood all around the body.   255

Hiccups happen when your lungs do not work quite right. Most hiccups   267
stop quickly, but some people's hiccups last a long time. One person had   280
hiccups for more than fifty years! Hiccups can be a problem because they   293
change the way we breathe.   298

To be healthy, we must take care of our lungs. For this reason, smoking is   313
very bad for them. They need exercise to stay healthy. When we exercise,   326
we make our lungs stronger. They are able to do their job better. They also   341
need clean air and rest to do their best work.   351

Calculation Boxes

	Reader 1		Reader 2	Reader 3
		Number of Words at Bracket		
		Subtract: Number of Words at Subhead	-79	-194
Number of Words at Bracket		Equals: Number of Words Attempted		
Subtract: Number of Errors	−	Subtract: Number of Errors	−	−
Equals: Words Correct per Minute (WCPM)		Equals: Words Correct per Minute (WCPM)		
Accuracy Percentage	%	Accuracy Percentage	%	%

Mark It!

1. p a s t
2. t r i p
3. h e l p
4. s t o p
5. f l a g
6. g l u m
7. s e n t
8. c r a m
9. p l o t
10. d r i p
11. t e n t h
12. l u n c h

Read It!

1. past	stop	sent
2. drip	trip	flag
3. cram	tenth	help
4. glum	plot	lunch
5. stop	drip	glum
6. help	flag	trip
7. tenth	sent	lunch
8. plot	cram	past

Underline digraphs with one line, blends with two separate lines, and digraph blends with one line under the consonant and one line under the digraph. Place a checkmark in the appropriate column, and circle the correct number of phonemes.

CHALLENGING

	Digraph	Blend	Digraph Blend	How many phonemes?			
1. <u>s</u>lip		✓		1	2	3	④
2. dish				1	2	3	4
3. jump				1	2	3	4
4. flat				1	2	3	4

MORE CHALLENGING

	Digraph	Blend	Digraph Blend	How many phonemes?			
5. shred				1	2	3	4
6. shot				1	2	3	4
7. elf				1	2	3	4
8. drum				1	2	3	4

MOST CHALLENGING

	Digraph	Blend	Digraph Blend	How many phonemes?			
9. stuck				1	2	3	4
10. lunch				1	2	3	4
11. swell				1	2	3	4
12. rush				1	2	3	4

CHALLENGING

1. could not be blunt (4)
2. will go west from here (5)
3. did not pick the round drum (6)
4. a speck of glass on the brim (7)

MORE CHALLENGING

5. drench the dish of French shrimp (6)
6. to plant the last bulb by the thrift shop (9)
7. did shred the mint with the lunch bunch (8)
8. will sit on the bench and munch on a stem (10)

CHALLENGING

1. Will you please grant me one last wish? (8)
2. Brad must rest at his desk to get his snack. (10)
3. When the glass fell off the grill, did it crack? (10)
4. The frog and the fish will jump in the small pond. (11)

MORE CHALLENGING

5. Val wept when the soft crust got black in the pan. (11)
6. Can you bend the tall twig and then grab the branch? (11)
7. I shrug when she asks if I know how to take out the trash. (14)
8. Did Nash flinch and duck when he saw the blue finch flash past the pond? (15)

SENTENCES

1. Read each sentence.
2. In Sentence 1, <u>underline</u> with separate lines the letters in the 2-sound blends.
3. In Sentence 2, draw a box around all the letters in the digraph blends.
4. Circle all the words that rhyme with **and**.

1 In the end, the plump elf will grant just one grand wish.

2 The grinch on the bench ate French shrimp for lunch and had to squint in the sun.

3 Drop the act, and lend a hand to the lost squid in the sand.

CHALLENGE YOURSELF

List <u>two</u> real words that rhyme with the following words.

mend	_____	_____
gust	_____	_____
blast	_____	_____
rent	_____	_____

Reader 1: _____   Date: _____

Reader 2: _____

Reader 3: _____

Words to Preview

Point & Say

1 **muscle** – an organ made up of tissues that produces movement in the body.
The muscles in my legs help me run quickly.

2 **heart rate** – how fast or slow the heart beats.
I was exercising, so my heart rate went up.

3 **digest** – to break food down in the body so it is usable.
After you eat a big meal, your stomach will digest the food into smaller pieces.

weigh

language

protects

Note: Hyphenated words count as one word.

The Brain

READER 1

The human brain is inside the skull. The hard skull protects the soft brain.	14
An adult brain weighs about three pounds. The brain has two sides. Both	27
sides are bumpy and gray. The brain looks a bit like a large, gray walnut.	42
There are many words for the brain. Some people call it the mind. Some	56
call it the noggin. They say, "You need to use your noggin!" Since the brain	71
is gray, sometimes people also call it "gray matter."	80

READER 2

The brain is not a muscle, but it acts like one in some ways. Just like with a	98
muscle, exercise helps the brain. The brain's exercise is different from other	110
exercise though. The brain gets exercise when a person thinks. You exercise	122
your brain when you think in new ways. You can read, work on puzzles, or	137
learn a new language. You can exercise your brain in many other ways, too.	151

READER 3

The brain takes care of everything in the body. The brain tells us if we are	167
hungry. It tells us if we are hot or cold. The brain is in charge of our senses:	185
sight, smell, hearing, touch, and taste. The brain is also in charge of what we	200
say and do. It tells us to say hello to a friend. It tells us to walk or jump. The	220
brain also controls your breathing, your heart rate, and digesting your food.	232

The human brain can do many things. It allows us to think, plan, speak,	246
move, cry, laugh, and dream. Take care of your brain. Eat healthy foods,	259
and get plenty of sleep. Make sure to wear a helmet if you ride a bike!	275
We only get one brain. It is our job to take care of it.	289

Calculation Boxes

	Reader 1		Reader 2	Reader 3
Number of Words at Bracket		Number of Words at Bracket		
		Subtract: Number of Words at Subhead	-80	-151
		Equals: Number of Words Attempted		
Subtract: Number of Errors	−	Subtract: Number of Errors	−	−
Equals: Words Correct per Minute (WCPM)		Equals: Words Correct per Minute (WCPM)		
Accuracy Percentage	%	Accuracy Percentage	%	%

Mark It!

1. j u d g e
2. s t r a p
3. m a t c h
4. f u d g e
5. s c r a p
6. s p l a s h
7. r i d g e
8. h u t c h
9. s p r i n t
10. w e d g e
11. s t r u c k
12. t e m p t

Read It!

1. judge   hutch   strap
2. match   fudge   splash
3. ridge   tempt   struck
4. scrap   wedge   sprint
5. strap   ridge   hutch
6. struck   judge   scrap
7. splash   sprint   wedge
8. fudge   match   tempt

Word Sort

Underline trigraphs with one line and 3-sound blends with three separate lines. Place a checkmark in the appropriate column, and circle the correct number of phonemes.

CHALLENGING

		Trigraph	3-Sound Blend	How many phonemes?					
1	le<u>dge</u>	✓		1	2	③	4	5	6
2	split			1	2	3	4	5	6
3	batch			1	2	3	4	5	6
4	strum			1	2	3	4	5	6

MORE CHALLENGING

		Trigraph	3-Sound Blend	How many phonemes?					
5	Dutch			1	2	3	4	5	6
6	scratch			1	2	3	4	5	6
7	botch			1	2	3	4	5	6
8	glitch			1	2	3	4	5	6

MOST CHALLENGING

		Trigraph	3-Sound Blend	How many phonemes?					
9	prompt			1	2	3	4	5	6
10	strict			1	2	3	4	5	6
11	script			1	2	3	4	5	6
12	splint			1	2	3	4	5	6

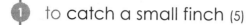

CHALLENGING

1. to catch a small finch (5)

2. sprint to the tall bridge (5)

3. did hatch a quick plan (5)

4. scrap the last math test (5)

MORE CHALLENGING

5. stretch and twist in bed (5)

6. fix the brass strap on my pack (7)

7. gasp and dodge the stench of trash (7)

8. will itch and scratch the patch on her back (9)

CHALLENGING

1. Fran will blush if her new pants split. (8)

2. Can we have lunch or brunch with Josh? (8)

3. Do not scratch the rash or you will get a scab. (11)

4. My Dutch frog will jump and splash in the ditch. (10)

MORE CHALLENGING

5. How fast can you sprint to the bridge and back to me? (12)

6. Rush to the top of the ridge and put a wedge in the back edge of the shed. (18)

7. Zack was hit in the chin with a quick pitch when he did not dodge the fast ball. (18)

8. Liz was with Mitch by the black splotch at the top of the ridge, and we saw them kiss. (19)

Word Creation

UNIT **3**

Add a trigraph or a 3-sound blend to either the beginning or the end of each word part to create a real word. There may be more than one correct answer.

Trigraphs
dge
tch

3-Sound Blends
str   spr
spl   scr
mpt

Word Parts	New Real Words	
1. ba	**badge**	
2. te		
3. ap		
4. pa		
5. pro		
6. twi		
7. at		
8. ing		

CHALLENGE YOURSELF

Combine a 3-sound blend and a trigraph with the given vowel to create a new word.

Word Parts	New Real Words
1. a	
2. e	
3. o	

Reader 1: _____   Date: _____

Reader 2: _____

Reader 3: _____

Words to Preview	Point & Say
① **organs** – parts of the body that perform specific functions, such as the heart that pumps blood, the lungs that breathe oxygen, and the liver that takes poisons out of the body. *The **organs** in the body, like the heart, lungs, and liver, keep our bodies working.*	joints protects
② **vital** – necessary or essential. *In order to stay healthy, it is **vital** to exercise and eat fruits and vegetables.*	
③ **fuse** – to join together. *Many bones **fuse** together as a child's body grows.*	
④ **calcium** – an element that is necessary for strong bones; calcium is found in dairy foods, such as milk, cheese, and yogurt, as well as in other foods, such as broccoli and salmon. *Bones need **calcium** to stay strong.*	

Note: Hyphenated words count as one word.

The Skeleton

READER 1

The skeleton is made up of the bones in a person's body. The skeleton gives	15
shape to the body.	19
Bones are hard and do not bend. A person's bones are very strong, but	33
they are also light because they have little holes inside them. The places	46
where they join are called joints. Joints help a person move in different	59
ways. Animals have skeletons, too. An animal's skeleton also helps it move	71
and gives shape to its body.	77

READER 2

The skeleton holds up a person's muscles and skin. It also protects the vital	91
organs. Vital organs are the organs that a person needs to live. The heart,	105
lungs, and brain are some of the vital organs.	114

All bones are important. The skull, ribs, and spine are some of the most   128
important bones. The skull is the hard bone that protects the brain. The skull   142
also gives shape to a person's face.   149

Ribs are long, thin bones. They are shaped like a cage. The rib cage   163
protects the heart, lungs, and other organs.   170

READER 3

The spine is a long group of bones along the back. It helps you stand up.   186
The spine and brain work together to help a person walk.   197

Babies have more bones than adults. An adult's skeleton has 206 bones.   209
A baby is born with about 300 bones. As a child grows, many of the bones   225
fuse together. A baby has a soft spot on the top of its head. The skull bones   242
have not joined together yet. These bones will fuse together by the time   255
the child is two.   259

It is important to keep bones strong. Bones need calcium. Calcium is found   272
in milk, cheese, broccoli, and other foods. Eating foods with calcium helps   284
keep bones strong. Exercise can also help keep bones strong. Exercise often   296
and eat foods with calcium to keep your skeleton strong.   306

Calculation Boxes

	Reader 1		Reader 2	Reader 3
		Number of Words at Bracket		
		Subtract: Number of Words at Subhead	-77	-170
Number of Words at Bracket		Equals: Number of Words Attempted		
Subtract: Number of Errors	−	Subtract: Number of Errors	−	−
Equals: Words Correct per Minute (WCPM)		Equals: Words Correct per Minute (WCPM)		
Accuracy Percentage	%	Accuracy Percentage	%	%

Mark It!

1. c a b | i n |
2. c o n f l i c t
3. r a d i s h
4. u n p l u g
5. c a t f i s h
6. f i n i s h
7. d e n t i s t
8. i n s e c t
9. b e d b u g
10. m i l k m a n
11. m a g n e t i c
12. v o l c a n i c

Read It!

1. cabin — unplug — dentist
2. milkman — conflict — radish
3. catfish — insect — magnetic
4. volcanic — finish — bedbug
5. unplug — radish — catfish
6. conflict — magnetic — cabin
7. bedbug — volcanic — finish
8. dentist — milkman — insect

Underline the vowels. Count the number of vowels to help you circle the correct number of syllables.

CHALLENGING

	How many syllables?	
1 limit	1	② 3
2 wish	1	2 3
3 laptop	1	2 3
4 split	1	2 3

MORE CHALLENGING

	How many syllables?	
5 epic	1	2 3
6 inhabit	1	2 3
7 tennis	1	2 3
8 chap	1	2 3

MOST CHALLENGING

	How many syllables?	
9 fantastic	1	2 3
10 basketball	1	2 3
11 inject	1	2 3
12 public	1	2 3

CHALLENGING

1. children had a contest (4)
2. will splash in my bathtub (5)
3. had eggnog in our cabin (5)
4. saw a mantis at the fishpond (6)

MORE CHALLENGING

5. catch the insect in the cobweb (6)
6. take a candid shot of the bobcat (7)
7. dentist will give a pretty plastic rabbit (7)
8. to help submit and publish the new script (8)

CHALLENGING

1. Lilith will bring a tennis racket to Memphis. (8)
2. You should limit how much you spend on a bobsled. (10)
3. Did I express that I cannot take a test at an unlit desk? (13)
4. How did all the catnip get into the cobwebs by the fridge? (12)

MORE CHALLENGING

5. Justin put the catfish and the plastic wombat in the bathtub. (11)
6. I think the traffic in Tibet will vanish after sunset, so do not stress. (14)
7. Will Ingrid zigzag to the annex after the fantastic athletic contest? (11)
8. Do not have a tantrum if your classic pumpkin from Wisconsin has a crack. (14)

Draw a line to connect the syllables that will spell a real word. Write the whole word on the line.

1. at   sect   **insect**
   gos   cot   _____
   in   tic   _____
   mas   sip   _____

2. ex   tis   _____
   ban   bag   _____
   hand dit   _____
   man   tend   _____

3. cob   cup   _____
   fab   top   _____
   hic   web   _____
   lap   ric   _____

4. con   dex   _____
   fin   test   _____
   in   ish   _____
   lim   it   _____

5. den   lock   _____
   nap   wich   _____
   sand kin   _____
   un   tist   _____

6. traf ish   _____
   dish nic   _____
   rad   fic   _____
   pic   pan   _____

CHALLENGE YOURSELF

Create new real words with these syllables. You may add a letter to the given syllable to form a new syllable. (Example: ten+d = tend; extend).

1. kin   **napkin**   _____   _____
2. top   **laptop**   _____   _____
3. ish   **radish**   _____   _____
4. ten   **extend**   _____   _____

Reader 1: _____   Date: _____

Reader 2: _____

Reader 3: _____

Words to Preview	Point & Say
1 **orbits** – moves around an object in space. *The Earth **orbits** the sun.*	metals
2 **satellite** – a smaller object that moves around a larger object in space. *The moon is a **satellite** of the Earth.*	
3 **reflects** – bounces off of a surface and then goes back toward the original object. *When I look in the mirror, it **reflects** my face.*	
4 **space capsule** – a small vehicle without wings that usually carries people into space. *The **space capsule** landed in the ocean after returning from the moon.*	

Note: Hyphenated words count as one word.

The Moon

READER 1

Most nights you can see the moon high in the sky. The moon is shaped like	16
a ball, just like the Earth. From Earth, the moon looks like it changes shape	31
throughout a month. On some nights, the moon is full. That means you can	45
see one round, lit side of the moon. On other nights you only see part of	61
the moon. Sometimes you cannot see the moon at all, but even when you	75
can't see the moon, it is still there.	83

READER 2

The moon shines, but it does not give off its own light. It reflects light from	99
the sun. On Earth, we see the light from the sun that shines on the moon.	115
Sometimes the moon is in a place where we can see the entire side of the	131
moon that is facing Earth. That is called a full moon. Sometimes we can't	145
see any light. It does not mean the moon is not in the sky. It only means that	163
we can't see any light reflected from the moon. When the moon is dark,	177
we call it a new moon.	183

READER 3

The moon orbits around the Earth, which means the moon is a satellite of	197
Earth. The moon takes about 28 days to circle the Earth. The moon always	211
takes the same path around the Earth. The path has an oval shape.	224

Like the Earth, the moon has rocks and metals. Unlike Earth, there is no	238
water on the moon. It is very hot during the day and very cold at night.	254
Nothing grows there. Nothing is able to live there.	263

In 1969, humans went to the moon for the first time. They rode in a space	279
capsule. Two men got out of a landing craft and walked on the moon.	293
People all over the world watched the first moonwalk on TV. It was the first	308
time anyone had left Earth and landed somewhere else in space.	319

Calculation Boxes

	Reader 1		Reader 2	Reader 3
Number of Words at Bracket		Number of Words at Bracket		
Subtract: Number of Errors	–	Subtract: Number of Words at Subhead	-83	-183
Equals: Words Correct per Minute (WCPM)		Equals: Number of Words Attempted		
Accuracy Percentage	%	Subtract: Number of Errors	–	–
		Equals: Words Correct per Minute (WCPM)		
		Accuracy Percentage	%	%

Mark It!

1. m e̲ n ⊔

2. b e g i n

3. s i l e n t

4. s e c r e t l y

5. m u s i c

6. p r o t e c t

7. b a b y

8. d e p e n d

9. r o b o t

10. z e r o

11. r e l a x

12. l a d y b u g

Read It!

1	menu	secretly	zero
2	relax	silent	depend
3	robot	begin	music
4	protect	ladybug	baby
5	zero	robot	begin
6	secretly	relax	menu
7	depend	protect	silent
8	music	baby	ladybug

Word Sort

Underline the vowels. Place a checkmark in the correct column for Closed or Open Syllable for each syllable.

CHALLENGING

	1st Syllable		2nd Syllable		3rd Syllable	
	Closed	Open	Closed	Open	Closed	Open
1. sh<u>y</u>		✓				
2. ban•jo						
3. e•vent•ful						
4. i•ris						

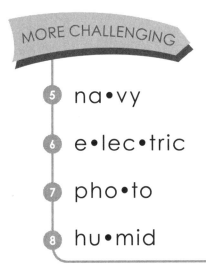

MORE CHALLENGING

	1st Syllable		2nd Syllable		3rd Syllable	
	Closed	Open	Closed	Open	Closed	Open
5. na•vy						
6. e•lec•tric						
7. pho•to						
8. hu•mid						

MOST CHALLENGING

	1st Syllable		2nd Syllable		3rd Syllable	
	Closed	Open	Closed	Open	Closed	Open
9. tri•pod						
10. po•ny						
11. vol•ca•no						
12. bun•ny						

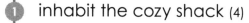

CHALLENGING

1. inhabit the cozy shack (4)
2. in the last basketball photo (5)
3. for the happy lady in the Navy (7)
4. a small decaf drink and a pastry (7)

MORE CHALLENGING

5. came down with a virus as a result (8)
6. will try to be silent and have respect (8)
7. put a new refreshment logo on the menu (8)
8. so plant the pretty lilac shrub beyond the bluff (9)

CHALLENGING

1. The happy but shy baby has spoken again. (8)
2. Can you defend and protect the chipmunk? (7)
3. My nylon wig gets frizzy when it is humid out. (10)
4. The fuzzy photo of Ivy and Enid is out of focus. (11)

MORE CHALLENGING

5. The banjo rock fest was eventful, but I was so hungry! (11)
6. Iris will be sly as she sprints by the robot rabbit in a rush. (14)
7. Enid was as silent as a jumbo jet when she was in the hotel. (14)
8. Which program do you want to try in Wisconsin, music or math? (12)

Place the missing consonant in the correct syllable for each word. Remember how closing a syllable or leaving it open will change the vowel sound. In the first example, placing the **m** in the first syllable makes the first syllable closed with a *short o* (**com ic**).

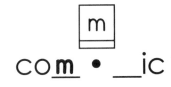

co**m** • __ic

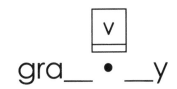

gra__ • __y

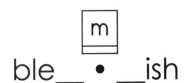

ble__ • __ish

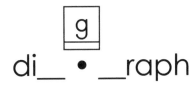

di__ • __raph

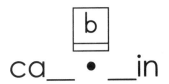

ca__ • __in

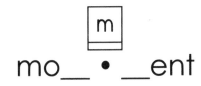

mo__ • __ent

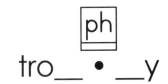

tro__ • __y

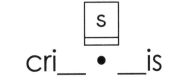

cri__ • __is

tu__ • __e__ • __o

do__ • __u__ • __ent

CHALLENGE YOURSELF

Write real words that fit the following syllable descriptions.

1. _____ _____
    open   closed

2. _____ _____
    open   closed

3. _____ _____ _____
    open   closed   closed

Reader 1: _____ Date: _____

Reader 2: _____

Reader 3: _____

Words to Preview	Point & Say
1 **billion** – a very large number that is equal to a thousand millions. *Stars can shine for **billions** of years.*	thousands millions
2 **gravity** – the force that pulls objects to each other. *Things fall to Earth because of **gravity**.*	
3 **energy** – usable heat or power. *The sun provides **energy** that supports life on Earth.*	
4 **dwarf** – something that is smaller than usual. *A **dwarf** star is smaller than other stars.*	

Note: Hyphenated words count as one word.

Stars

READER 1

At night, we can see thousands of stars in the sky. The stars we see are	16
billions of miles away. There are millions more stars that are so far away that	31
we can't see them. Many other stars are too small or dim for us to see.	47

The sun is the only star we see during the day. The sun is a star even though	65
it looks different from the rest of the stars. This is because the sun is much	81
closer to us.	84

READER 2

Stars are huge balls of very hot gases. They burn and give off light and heat.	100
When we see a star from Earth, we are seeing the gases burning. Stars can	115
shine for billions of years.	120

Most stars look the same color from Earth. They really are different colors	133
though. Stars are red, orange, yellow, white, or blue. A star's color is based	147
on how hot the star is. The hottest and brightest stars are called blue giants.	162
The cooler stars are red. Even red stars are very hot.	173

READER 3

A star begins life in a huge cloud of gases and dust. After millions of years,	189
gravity pulls the dust and gases toward each other. The dust and gases	202
start to stick together. The star gets hotter as it becomes larger. It grows	216
hot enough to give off energy. That energy is the light we see when a	231
star shines.	233

During its life, a star will burn two or three kinds of gas. When a star is millions	251
of years old, one kind of gas starts to get used up. A different gas in the	268
center of the star begins to burn. The star gets smaller, and it dims as it shrinks.	285

Then the star slowly cools. The outside part gets bigger and turns redder.	298
The star is then called a red giant.	306

Lastly, the outer layers of the star drift off into space. The small center that is	322
left is called a white dwarf. It shines weakly for billions of years as it cools.	338

Calculation Boxes

	Reader 1		Reader 2	Reader 3
Number of Words at Bracket		Number of Words at Bracket		
		Subtract: Number of Words at Subhead	-84	-173
		Equals: Number of Words Attempted		
Subtract: Number of Errors	−	Subtract: Number of Errors	−	−
Equals: Words Correct per Minute (WCPM)		Equals: Words Correct per Minute (WCPM)		
Accuracy Percentage	%	Accuracy Percentage	%	%

Mark It!

1. @t t a̲ c h
2. b a s k e t
3. s a l a d
4. a d u l t
5. w i s d o m
6. c a p i t a l
7. p a j a m a s
8. v e l v e t
9. l e m o n
10. m a m m a l
11. g a l l o n
12. p r a c t i c a l

Read It!

1. attach	capital	wisdom
2. basket	adult	lemon
3. mammal	practical	velvet
4. gallon	pajamas	salad
5. wisdom	mammal	adult
6. capital	gallon	basket
7. velvet	lemon	practical
8. salad	attach	pajamas

Place a checkmark in the correct column for Closed or Open Syllable for each syllable.
Circle the vowel letter that spells the *schwa* sound.

CHALLENGING

	1st Syllable		2nd Syllable		3rd Syllable	
	Closed	Open	Closed	Open	Closed	Open
1 drag•on	✓		✓			
2 cot•ton						
3 buf•fa•lo						
4 a•cross						

MORE CHALLENGING

	1st Syllable		2nd Syllable		3rd Syllable	
	Closed	Open	Closed	Open	Closed	Open
5 vil•la						
6 fal•con						
7 a•pron						
8 mag•net						

MOST CHALLENGING

	1st Syllable		2nd Syllable		3rd Syllable	
	Closed	Open	Closed	Open	Closed	Open
9 oc•ta•gon						
10 bas•ket•ball						
11 max•i•mum						
12 a•dop•ted						

CHALLENGING

1. children and adults left (4)
2. saw the label on the relish (6)
3. basic frozen lemon punch (4)
4. program will happen soon (4)

MORE CHALLENGING

5. all of your tiny new vitamins (6)
6. the last volcano on Venus erupted (6)
7. ate more than a dozen bagel sandwiches (7)
8. take a splendid black and white photograph (7)

CHALLENGING

1. Walk to the old zebra and rabbit habitat. (8)
2. Quinn will model the classic, satin navy dress. (8)
3. To find the secret jumbo gift, look under the tall shelf. (11)
4. Can you please hand me the gravy and the utensils? (10)

MORE CHALLENGING

5. I want to see Greta, a yellow dragon, in the frozen tundra. (12)
6. The puny tropical cactus was in the plastic pot by the shovel. (12)
7. When you see a gallon trashcan, toss the rest of the spinach salad. (13)
8. My dog, Brenda, will attend to any command you give in an instant. (13)

Add a word beginning or a word ending to each word part to create a real word. The word beginnings and endings each contain a *schwa* sound.

Word Beginnings

com
con
a

Word Endings

a	et
on	al
en	us

Word Parts

1. bo*n **us**
2. ___*fess
3. ___*dult
4. lo*c___
5. e*v___
6. ___*la*sk___
7. gal*l___
8. ___*mand
9. fro*z___
10. a*ban*d___

New Real Words

1. **bonus**
2. _____
3. _____
4. _____
5. _____
6. _____
7. _____
8. _____
9. _____
10. _____

CHALLENGE YOURSELF

Choose **two** words from above, and write **one** sentence that includes both of those words on the lines below.

_____

_____

Reader 1: _____   Date: _____

Reader 2: _____

Reader 3: _____

Words to Preview	**Point & Say**

1 **solar system** – the sun, planets, and other objects that move around the sun.
*Earth is a planet in our **solar system**.*

2 **scientists** – people who study the structure and behavior of the physical and natural world.
*Those **scientists** know a lot about the solar system.*

3 **eclipse** – an event in space when the light from one object is blocked by another.
*The moon blocked the light from the sun to create an **eclipse**.*

4 **partial** – not complete.
*A **partial** eclipse does not cover the whole sun.*

Point & Say:

billions

sunspots

thousands

Note: Hyphenated words count as one word.

The Sun

READER 1

The sun is a star at the center of our solar system. Solar means "having to do   17
with the sun." Earth and all the planets in our solar system orbit around the   32
sun. That means that Earth travels around the sun. The sun is closer to Earth   47
than other stars. This is why the sun looks like a round yellow ball. Other stars   63
look much smaller because they are not as close.   72

READER 2

Just like other stars, the sun gives off light and heat. That is why people,   87
plants, and animals are able to live on Earth.   96

Scientists use special cameras to take pictures of the sun. These pictures   108
show that the sun is a mass of burning gas. The pictures also show that the   124
gas swirls around as it burns. Pictures of the sun show dark patches called   138
sunspots. Sunspots form where the gas is cooler than the rest of the sun.   152
Sunspots are still very hot, though. Sunspots are often seen in groups. The   165
groups can stretch sixty thousand miles or more from one end to another.   178

READER 3

Sometimes the moon passes between Earth and the sun. When this	189
happens, the moon blocks the light from the sun. This is called a solar	203
eclipse. Each solar eclipse can only be seen from certain places on Earth.	216
These are the places that are in the shadow cast by the moon.	229

Two or three solar eclipses happen every year. Most of the time, the moon	243
does not block all of the sun's light. This is called a partial eclipse.	257
Once every year or two, the moon blocks the whole sun. This is called	272
a total eclipse.	275

Like all stars, our sun has a life cycle. It still has another five billion years	291
to shine strongly. After about five billion years, the sun will age into a red	306
giant. Next, it will cool off to become a white dwarf. Billions of years later,	321
the white dwarf will be cool. At that time, the sun will turn into a cold, dark	338
body called a black dwarf.	342

Calculation Boxes

	Reader 1		Reader 2	Reader 3
Number of Words at Bracket		Number of Words at Bracket		
Subtract: Number of Errors	−	Subtract: Number of Words at Subhead	-72	-178
Equals: Words Correct per Minute (WCPM)		Equals: Number of Words Attempted		
Accuracy Percentage	%	Subtract: Number of Errors	−	−
		Equals: Words Correct per Minute (WCPM)		
		Accuracy Percentage	%	%

Mark It!

1. c o m p e t e
2. a m a z e
3. c a m p s i t e
4. a m u s e
5. c u p c a k e
6. d i v i d e
7. e n v e l o p e
8. v o l u m e
9. s u n s h i n e
10. m e d i c a t e
11. p a r a d e
12. p o l i t e

Read It!

1. compete
2. envelope
3. polite
4. volume
5. medicate
6. cupcake
7. amuse
8. amaze

amuse
amaze
divide
parade
envelope
sunshine
campsite
divide

medicate
sunshine
campsite
cupcake
polite
compete
parade
volume

Which Syllable Is Which?

Write each syllable in the correct column. The vowel letters that spell *schwa* are circled.

CHALLENGING

1. tad•pole
2. skate
3. fire•m(a)n
4. mi•grate

Closed	Open	VCE
tad		**pole**

MORE CHALLENGING

5. o•zone
6. style
7. r(e)•fuse
8. ath•lete

Closed	Open	VCE

MOST CHALLENGING

9. an•t(e)•lope
10. ep•(i)•sode
11. quake
12. hom•(o)•phone

Closed	Open	VCE

CHALLENGING

1. safe to erase the last name (6)

2. will explode and make smoke (5)

3. a good pancake at lunchtime (5)

4. too lazy to use the secret handshake (7)

MORE CHALLENGING

5. can locate the wide wishbone inside (6)

6. reptile sits upon a jade stone in the cave (9)

7. is impolite to chase Pete into the concrete maze (9)

8. gaze at the base of the Japanese lamp by my bedside (11)

CHALLENGING

1. Is it insane to refuse a milkshake and a cupcake? (10)

2. Visit the website to translate that phrase into Spanish. (9)

3. Dave forgave Jane when she was late for the episode. (10)

4. Kate, open the wide white envelope beside the tadpole dish. (10)

MORE CHALLENGING

5. If I calculate the total for you, will you make me a kale salad? (14)

6. Did you type a note to make up for the broken stoneware pancake pan? (14)

7. You must locate the capital of every state in the United States by the time the flame is out. (19)

8. I smile widely when I think back to the sunshine and the amazing landscape by the Ambrose Hotel. (18)

Draw a line to connect the word parts in the first column with the VCE spellings in the second column that will spell a real word. Write the whole word on the line.

1. wh   ide   **slide** _____

    mis*t   ape   _____

    gr   ite   _____

    sl   ake   _____

2. th   one   _____

    lo*c   eme   _____

    ph   ope   _____

    sl   ate   _____

3. gr   ake   _____

    str   ute   _____

    qu   ade   _____

    com*p   ide   _____

4. web*s   ide   _____

    fl   eme   _____

    in*s   ite   _____

    ex*tr   ame   _____

5. cup*c   ale   _____

    ex*h   ete   _____

    on*l   ake   _____

    com*p   ine   _____

6. mi*gr   ume   _____

    in*v   ake   _____

    vol*   ite   _____

    pan*c   ate   _____

CHALLENGE YOURSELF

Create as many new real words as you can with the following vowel-consonant-e endings.

1   ade _____   _____

    _____   _____

2   one _____   _____

    _____   _____

Reader 1: _____   Date: _____

Reader 2: _____

Reader 3: _____

Words to Preview	Point & Say
1 **identify** – to recognize and be able to say who someone is or what something is. *I was able to **identify** the clouds by their shapes.*	mare vapor
2 **Latin** – the language of ancient Rome. *Some people study **Latin** even though it is no longer a spoken language.*	
3 **cumulus** – (pronounced kyoom-yuh-luhs) a fluffy cloud made of white masses piled on each other. *The **cumulus** clouds look like cotton balls.*	
4 **stratus** – (pronounced strat-uhs) a cloud forming a flat gray sheet. *The **stratus** clouds are like a blanket in the sky.*	
5 **cirrus** – (pronounced sear-uhs) a high, long, thin cloud. *The **cirrus** clouds are wispy and high.*	

Note: Hyphenated words count as one word.

Clouds

READER 1

Clouds are water in a different form. They usually float high in the sky,	14
but sometimes they touch the ground. We call these low clouds fog. We	27
identify clouds by their shape and how high they are from the ground.	40
Clouds have three main shapes. There are other cloud shapes, though.	51
Most of the other cloud shapes are some mix of the three main types of	66
clouds. The names for the three main cloud shapes come from Latin.	78
The meanings of the Latin names tell us what the clouds look like.	91

READER 2

One cloud shape is called cumulus. That means "heap" in Latin. Cumulus	103
clouds are white and fluffy, and they look like cotton balls. They are caused	117
by rising warm air. These clouds can get very tall.	127

Another cloud shape is called stratus. Stratus means "layer" in Latin. Stratus	139
clouds spread across the sky in a wide, flat layer. They can look like a big	155
blanket in the sky.	159

The third main cloud shape is cirrus. Cirrus means "curl of hair" in Latin.	173
Cirrus clouds look like thin wisps in the sky. They are sometimes called mare's	187
tails because they can look like the tail of a horse.	198

READER 3

Clouds are also identified by how high they are from the ground. There are	212
low, mid, and high-level clouds. Low clouds are closest to the ground. They	225
are usually made of water droplets. The bottoms of mid-level clouds are	237
between 6,500 and 20,000 feet above the ground. High-level clouds are so	249
high that they are usually made of ice crystals.	258

Some clouds get so tall that they are in two or three levels. Cumulus and	273
stratus clouds can be low, mid, or high-level clouds. Cirrus clouds are only	286
found high above the ground.	291

Clouds are made when water turns from a liquid into a gas. The gas is	306
called water vapor. As the water vapor rises, it cools and turns into droplets.	320
The droplets cling to tiny bits of dust in the air. The droplets can be water or	337
ice. This depends on how cold the air is.	346

When billions of droplets come together, they form the clouds you see in	359
the sky. When the droplets in the clouds grow too heavy, they fall to Earth.	374
They may fall as rain, snow, or sleet.	382

Calculation Boxes

	Reader 1		Reader 2	Reader 3
Number of Words at Bracket		Number of Words at Bracket		
Subtract: Number of Errors	–	Subtract: Number of Words at Subhead	-91	-198
Equals: Words Correct per Minute (WCPM)		Equals: Number of Words Attempted		
Accuracy Percentage	%	Subtract: Number of Errors	–	–
		Equals: Words Correct per Minute (WCPM)		
		Accuracy Percentage	%	%

Mark It!

1. o l i v e
2. t e m p l a t e
3. f e s t i v e
4. c o t t a g e
5. p a l a c e
6. p a c k a g e
7. a t t e n t i v e
8. l u g g a g e
9. m e s s a g e
10. p i r a t e
11. a c t i v e
12. e x p l o s i v e

Read It!

1. olive
2. attentive
3. pirate
4. luggage
5. palace
6. explosive
7. package
8. cottage

palace
active
package
cottage
message
luggage
festive
template

explosive
message
festive
template
pirate
active
attentive
olive

Which Syllable Is Which?

Write each syllable in the correct column. The *schwa* spellings are circled.

CHALLENGING

1. pas•s(age)
2. na•(tive)
3. cab•b(age)
4. pave•m(e)nt

Closed	Open	VCE
pas		**sage**

MORE CHALLENGING

5. in•flate
6. re•pack•(age)
7. pri•v(ate)
8. cap•(ti)•vate

Closed	Open	VCE

MOST CHALLENGING

9. del•(i)•c(ate)
10. steth•(o)•scope
11. re•pul•s(ive)
12. frus•trate

Closed	Open	VCE

CHALLENGING

1. ate some cabbage at lunchtime (5)
2. made a disgusting olive cupcake (5)
3. the secretive unit at our campsite (6)
4. pirate will manage to escape the trap (7)

MORE CHALLENGING

5. will have a positive time at the parade (8)
6. did hope to live in a private Chinese palace (9)
7. ape is native to the massive mangrove thicket (8)
8. repulsive garbage will bake in the hot sunshine (8)

CHALLENGING

1. The wind damage to the lonely cottage was quite extensive. (10)
2. Our passage across the uneven lake to the village was difficult. (11)
3. I put my printed image and my package in a secret safe on campus. (14)
4. Do not rummage in my grandma's closet to find her private candy stash. (13)

MORE CHALLENGING

5. You could invite Miss Vandike to the festive parade by our cottage. (12)
6. Pete is motivated to pass the secretive message on to Nate the pirate. (13)
7. The advantage of this type of luggage is that it has extra side pockets. (14)
8. Will you have to repackage the delicate Japanese glass globe from Jolene? (12)

WORDS

1. Read each word.
2. <u>Underline</u> and connect the vowels in the VCE spelling patterns that spell the *schwa* sound.
3. Draw a box around the words that rhyme with **fit**.
4. Circle all the words that have **three** syllables.

cottage	chocolate	detective
palace	negative	reptile
private	landscape	positive
mistake	village	umpire
passage	climate	festive

CHALLENGE YOURSELF

1. Find the word that contains a digraph. _____

2. Find 2 words that refer to jobs.

   _____   _____

3. Find 3 words that are places where you can live.

   _____   _____   _____

4. Find the word that is the opposite of positive. _____

Reader 1: _____   Date: _____

Reader 2: _____

Reader 3: _____

Words to Preview	Point & Say
1 **comets** – frozen balls of ice, dust, and gases that orbit the sun. *Many of the comets in space cannot be seen from Earth.*	Edmond Halley
2 **core** – middle. *The core of a comet is made of dust and gas.*	scientist
3 **Jupiter** – the largest planet in our solar system. *The planet Jupiter has four large moons and many smaller moons.*	
4 **Halley's Comet** – (Halley rhymes with valley) the most famous comet; it appears about every 76 years. *Halley's Comet was last seen in 1986.*	

Note: Hyphenated words count as one word.

Comets

READER 1

We can see comets in the night sky. Some people call comets dirty	13
snowballs. That is because they are made of ice, dust, and gases. You	26
cannot throw these dirty snowballs. Comets are much too big to throw.	38
They are huge objects in space. The core of a comet can be the size of	54
the planet Jupiter.	57

Comets orbit the sun. They follow a path shaped like an egg. Comets travel	71
millions of miles into the outer parts of our solar system. Some comets come	85
so close to Earth that we can see them.	94

READER 2

Many comets have what look like long, bright tails. The tails are formed as	108
a comet nears the sun. The core of a comet is frozen. The sun's heat turns	124
some of the frozen core into gas. The gas and dust form a comet's tail.	139
The tail can be millions of miles long.	147

Each time a comet orbits the sun, it loses some of the gases and dust from | 163
its tail. Most comets break up and vanish after they pass by the sun a few | 179
hundred times. That is because they lose so much gas and dust that they | 193
no longer exist. | 196

READER 3

For many years, people did not understand comets. They did not show up | 209
in regular patterns like the sun, moon, and stars. Some people even thought | 222
that comets brought bad luck. | 227

In 1705, a scientist found out something about comets. He proved that | 239
comets orbit the sun. This helped people understand more about comets. | 250

The man who made the discovery was Edmond Halley. He studied comets. | 262
The most famous comet is named after him. It is called Halley's Comet. This | 276
comet was around long before Halley was born. We have very old records | 289
that tell about people seeing this well-known comet. Some of the records | 301
are more than 2,000 years old! | 307

We can only see Halley's Comet when it comes close enough to Earth. | 320
That happens about every 76 years. It will be close to Earth again in 2061. | 335
During that time, we may learn even more about this special comet. | 347

Calculation Boxes

Number of Words at Bracket	Reader 1	Number of Words at Bracket	Reader 2	Reader 3
		Subtract: Number of Words at Subhead	-94	-196
		Equals: Number of Words Attempted		
Subtract: Number of Errors	–	Subtract: Number of Errors	–	–
Equals: Words Correct per Minute (WCPM)		Equals: Words Correct per Minute (WCPM)		
Accuracy Percentage	%	Accuracy Percentage	%	%

Mark It!

1. det<u>ai</u>l
2. coastal
3. crayfish
4. highway
5. rainbow
6. speechless
7. unbraid
8. toasty
9. unsightly
10. display
11. complain
12. agreed

Read It!

1. detail
2. unsightly
3. unbraid
4. coastal
5. display
6. agreed
7. rainbow
8. highway

display
agreed
speechless
complain
crayfish
toasty
detail
unsightly

toasty
crayfish
highway
rainbow
coastal
unbraid
speechless
complain

▶ Word Sort

Circle the correct number of syllables, and write the long vowel spellings in the appropriate columns for all long vowels. Some words may have more than one long vowel phoneme, and not all of the long vowel spellings will be vowel teams. The vowel letters that spell *schwa* are circled.

CHALLENGING

	How many syllables?	/ā/	/ē/	/ī/	/ō/
1. fright	① 2 3			**igh**	
2. b(e)low	1 2 3				
3. c(o)mplain	1 2 3				
4. frisbee	1 2 3				

MORE CHALLENGING

	How many syllables?	/ā/	/ē/	/ī/	/ō/
5. oatmeal	1 2 3				
6. grownup	1 2 3				
7. daisy	1 2 3				
8. detail	1 2 3				

MOST CHALLENGING

	How many syllables?	/ā/	/ē/	/ī/	/ō/
9. trainload	1 2 3				
10. throw(a)way	1 2 3				
11. prepay	1 2 3				
12. explaining	1 2 3				

CHALLENGING

1. drink hot cocoa near the whaleboat (6)

2. train began the delay on the highway (7)

3. sprint to the rainbow near the oak tree (8)

4. plenty of baseball bats and gear to play with (9)

MORE CHALLENGING

5. put on a yellow peacoat or my new raincoat (9)

6. made a career out of patching king-size bedsheets (8)

7. obtain and clean the queen's silky green night dress (9)

8. roaming in a jeep to find a toad in the shallow pond (12)

CHALLENGING

1. There are fifteen throwaway canteens in the cabin. (8)

2. Colleen felt a slight scratch in her throat at bedtime. (10)

3. I will shine the brightest flashlight so we can see the leak. (12)

4. If we sweep the streets, we will help keep our state clean. (12)

MORE CHALLENGING

5. Their goal is to remain upbeat, despite the rain and hail, while they travel. (14)

6. Steve will reclaim the expensive oval ring from the bottom of the deep creek bed. (15)

7. Jay was speechless after seeing the play with the fair and faithful Jeep salesman. (14)

8. The moat beside the palace will keep the inhabitants safe from the sneaky coachmen. (14)

WORDS

1. Read each word.
2. <u>Underline</u> words that contain the same vowel phoneme as the word **bite**.
3. Draw a boxed(box) around the words that contain the *long e* phoneme.
4. Circle all the vowel teams that spell *long a*.

complain	between	frightful
hungry	cocoa	repay
snowdrift	repeated	oatmeal
sight	paintbrush	peanut
playful	fifteen	approach

CHALLENGE YOURSELF

1. Find the word with two vowel teams. _____

2. Find the word that explains how you might feel before lunch.

   _____

3. Find 2 words that are things you can eat.

   _____   _____

4. Find the word that means "to walk up to." _____

Reader 1: _____   Date: _____

Reader 2: _____

Reader 3: _____

Words to Preview	**Point & Say**

1. **predators** – animals that hunt other animals for food.
   Predators, such as larger fish or raptors, hunt small fish to eat.

2. **frigid** – very cold.
   *The ocean water at the New Jersey shore is **frigid** in January.*

3. **cold-blooded** – having a body temperature that matches the surroundings.
   *The **cold-blooded** snake slithered through the forest toward the sun to keep warm.*

4. **dwarf goby** – (goby rhymes with Toby) one of the smallest fish in the sea.
   *The **dwarf goby** swims away from the hungry shark.*

Point & Say

gills

ocean

temperature

Note: Hyphenated words count as one word.

Fish

READER 1

There are more than 28,000 kinds of fish that live all around the world.	14
Some live close to land, and others live in deep water. Some fish live in the	30
salt water of seas and oceans. Other fish live in the fresh water of lakes,	45
rivers, and ponds.	48
Fish are animals that live in the water. Most fish have scales to protect them.	63
They use fins and tails to move through the water. They use gills to breathe	78
under water.	80

READER 2

Most fish lay eggs. Some make their nests in rocks or plants. Others just lay	95
their eggs in the water. Some fish lay many eggs, but not all the eggs will	111
hatch. Predators will eat some of them. Others will not hatch because the	124
water is too warm or too cold. When eggs hatch, the young fish are still at	140
risk. Water that is too hot or cold can kill baby fish. Predators also eat many	156
young fish. Very few eggs will become adult fish.	165

60

READER 3

Fish breathe through gills. The gills take oxygen from the water to help	178
fish breathe. This is different from the way many other animals breathe.	190
Not everything that lives in the water is a fish. Dolphins, whales, jellyfish,	203
and starfish are not really fish.	209
Some kinds of fish swim in groups called schools. Fish are safer when they	223
swim in schools. They work together to watch for danger. Also, the small fish	237
look bigger to predators when they are together.	245
The biggest fish is the whale shark. It can grow up to 60 feet long. One of	262
the smallest fish is the dwarf goby. It is less than half an inch long.	277
Most fish are cold-blooded. This means their temperatures change with	287
the temperature of the water where they swim. Some fish live only in warm	301
waters. Others live only in cold waters. Fish that live in frigid temperatures	314
can even live in water that has ice on the top.	325

Calculation Boxes

	Reader 1		Reader 2	Reader 3
Number of Words at Bracket		Number of Words at Bracket		
Subtract: Number of Errors	–	Subtract: Number of Words at Subhead	-80	-165
Equals: Words Correct per Minute (WCPM)		Equals: Number of Words Attempted		
Accuracy Percentage	%	Subtract: Number of Errors	–	–
		Equals: Words Correct per Minute (WCPM)		
		Accuracy Percentage	%	%

Mark It!

1. h o c k <u>e y</u>
2. l a d i e s
3. b e l i e f
4. c h i m n e y
5. f i e l d t r i p
6. w i n d s h i e l d
7. a l l e y
8. d i e s e l
9. b a b i e s
10. m e d l e y
11. c a s h i e r
12. v o l l e y b a l l

Read It!

1. hockey — belief — babies
2. medley — ladies — windshield
3. volleyball — fieldtrip — alley
4. chimney — diesel — cashier
5. babies — volleyball — ladies
6. windshield — hockey — medley
7. alley — cashier — diesel
8. belief — chimney — fieldtrip

Word Sort

Circle the correct number of syllables, and write the long vowel spellings in the appropriate columns for all long vowels. Some words may have more than one long vowel phoneme, and not all of the long vowel spellings will be vowel teams. The vowel letters that spell *schwa* are circled.

CHALLENGING

	How many syllables?			/ā/	/ē/	/ī/	/ō/
1 brief	①	2	3		**ie**		
2 backseat	1	2	3				
3 key	1	2	3				
4 windowpane	1	2	3				

MORE CHALLENGING

	How many syllables?			/ā/	/ē/	/ī/	/ō/
5 volley	1	2	3				
6 dream	1	2	3				
7 soapy	1	2	3				
8 roadside	1	2	3				

MOST CHALLENGING

	How many syllables?			/ā/	/ē/	/ī/	/ō/
9 shadow	1	2	3				
10 sunscreen	1	2	3				
11 yellowtail	1	2	3				
12 showm(a)nship	1	2	3				

CHALLENGING

1. will donate lilies, posies, or lilacs (6)

2. messy chimney needs a cleaning (5)

3. pays to stay in a clean, cheery motel (8)

4. sits in the backseat of the speedboat (7)

MORE CHALLENGING

5. need to find cash to pay for a new fishbowl (10)

6. a chutney and baloney sandwich on the trolley (8)

7. roaming in a jeep to find jelly for my chimpanzee (10)

8. had a big fight while coaching the baseball team (9)

CHALLENGING

1. My mom uses an oatmeal treatment for her itchy skin. (10)

2. The plane delay will make us late for the freedom rally in Philly. (13)

3. Will you be attending the Greek eating event in the bungalow? (11)

4. Amy has her pillow and plenty of games, so now she can sleep at Janeen's. (15)

MORE CHALLENGING

5. We keep honeybees so we can sweeten our cakes and cookies. (11)

6. Mickey, the cashier at the Coastline Grill, divides the meat for sandwiches. (12)

7. After we get back from bowling, I need to feed beets and cocoa to my happy gray donkey, Bailey. (19)

8. The little insect on our windshield was so distracting that we had to pull right over to the side of the road and clean it off. (26)

SENTENCES

1. Read each sentence.
2. In Sentence 1, underline all of the vowel teams.
3. Draw a box around all the vowel team spellings of *long e*.
4. Circle the word that contains the *long o* sound twice.

1 I am not afraid of shadows at night when I have my flashlight.

2 I wept when I lost my keys and all of my pennies beneath the willow tree.

3 I like hot cocoa and raisin oatmeal for brunch on the weekends.

CHALLENGE YOURSELF

Using your knowledge of long vowel spellings, come up with three words that contain each long vowel phoneme listed below. To make the challenge more difficult, use a different spelling of the long vowel phoneme in each word. Do not use words from the sentences above.

long i	frightful	hide	silent
long a	_____	_____	_____
long e	_____	_____	_____
long o	_____	_____	_____

Reader 1: _____   Date: _____

Reader 2: _____

Reader 3: _____

Words to Preview	Point & Say
1 **mammals** – warm-blooded animals with a backbone; females produce milk to feed their young. *Mammals such as cows, dogs, and horses feed their babies with milk their bodies make.*	trouble
2 **aquatic** – living in water. *Starfish are one of many aquatic creatures.*	scales
3 **communicate** – to share information. *Talking and emailing are ways people communicate with each other.*	ocean

Note: Hyphenated words count as one word.

Sea Mammals

READER 1

Sea animals come in all shapes and sizes. Most people think of fish when	14
they think of aquatic animals. There are many other kinds of sea animals,	27
too. Some of them are mammals. Whales, seals, and dolphins are three	39
kinds of sea mammals.	43

Fish and sea mammals are different in many ways. Fish are covered in scales,	57
while mammals have no scales. Fish can stay underwater because they	68
breathe through gills. Mammals may hold their breath for a very long time,	81
but they must come up for air.	88

READER 2

Fish are cold-blooded, but mammals are warm-blooded. Sea mammals	97
can stay warm in cold water. Whales, seals, and dolphins have thick fat on	111
their bodies. This fat keeps them warm enough to live in very cold water.	125
They would die from the cold without this fat.	134

Fish lay eggs, but sea mammals are born live. Whales, dolphins, and seals	147
feed milk to their young. They care for their young for many months. They	161
teach them how to hunt for food and how to stay safe.	173

READER 3

Whales, seals, and dolphins use sound to communicate with their young.	184
Whales sing songs to their young. Seals bark in a way that sounds a lot like	200
dogs. Dolphins click to their young.	206

Whales, seals, and dolphins are friendly animals. If they feel safe, they do	219
not hurt people. Dolphins sometimes save people in the ocean who are	231
in trouble. They may pull these people back to land. They may also save	245
people from sharks.	248

Humans can watch sea mammals in many settings. Sea mammals	258
sometimes put on shows for people. Seals perform tricks and dolphins put	270
on shows at many water parks. People can even swim with dolphins in	283
some places. Many people go on boat trips to watch whales. People are	296
thrilled when they see whales jump or blow water into the air.	308

Calculation Boxes

	Reader 1		Reader 2	Reader 3
		Number of Words at Bracket		
		Subtract: Number of Words at Subhead	-88	-173
Number of Words at Bracket		Equals: Number of Words Attempted		
Subtract: Number of Errors	−	Subtract: Number of Errors	−	−
Equals: Words Correct per Minute (WCPM)		Equals: Words Correct per Minute (WCPM)		
Accuracy Percentage	%	Accuracy Percentage	%	%

Mark It!

1. a r t i s t
2. s t a r v i n g
3. c o r n m e a l
4. f o r g a v e
5. a p a r t
6. o r b i t
7. c a r t w h e e l
8. p i t c h f o r k
9. b a c k y a r d
10. s t a r t e d
11. t h o r n y
12. t a r g e t

Read It!

1. artist	cornmeal	target
2. thorny	pitchfork	apart
3. backyard	orbit	starving
4. forgave	cartwheel	started
5. target	thorny	cornmeal
6. pitchfork	artist	backyard
7. started	starving	cartwheel
8. apart	forgave	orbit

Which Syllable Is Which?

Write each syllable in the correct column. The *schwa* spellings are circled.

CHALLENGING

1. r(e)•mark
2. for•g(i)ve•n(e)ss
3. r(e)•port
4. in•form

Closed	Open	VCE	Vowel Team	R-Controlled
	re			mark

MORE CHALLENGING

5. north•west
6. ar•cade
7. char•coal
8. d(e)•part•m(e)nt

Closed	Open	VCE	Vowel Team	R-Controlled

MOST CHALLENGING

9. r(e)•gard•l(e)ss
10. or•g(a)•nize
11. ar•t(i)•choke
12. or•n(a)•m(e)nt

Closed	Open	VCE	Vowel Team	R-Controlled

CHALLENGING

1. when the acorn falls from the tree (7)
2. embark on a boat in the darkness (7)
3. had a boring horse ride in a rainstorm (8)
4. spark a chat with my smartest classmate (7)

MORE CHALLENGING

5. cannot deprive a starving shark of meat (7)
6. find a normal meat market north of here (8)
7. quickly need a new passport to fly to Norway (9)
8. will have to clean the artichoke green carpet (8)

CHALLENGING

1. We will march in protest of the unfair potato embargo. (10)
2. Glenda started to do a cartwheel in the carnival yard. (10)
3. Dora will scorch her short organza dress if she gets distracted. (11)
4. I cannot wait to travel from snowy New York to sunny Florida this weekend! (14)

MORE CHALLENGING

5. Some armadillos live in the marshes, or wetlands, of the United States. (12)
6. Martha has artistic talent that will make her the star harpist at the park festival. (15)
7. Quick, fetch Mister Davenport a plastic fork from the hotdog cart across from Markus Park. (15)
8. The harsh wind made Barlow think a scarf was needed for his trip to the harvest festival. (17)

WORDS

1. Read each word.
2. <u>Underline</u> words that do not have any r-controlled vowels.
3. Draw a box around the words that have three syllables.
4. Circle the word that has two r-controlled vowels.

target	backyard	afraid
smartest	popcorn	formula
trombone	horses	garden
Oregon	harvested	pardon
cornstarch	parking	erase

CHALLENGE YOURSELF

1. Find the word for something you can ride. _____

2. Find the word that means the same as "most intelligent."

_____

3. Find 3 words that are locations.

_____ _____ _____

4. Find the word that is something you aim for. _____

Reader 1: _____ Date: _____

Reader 2: _____

Reader 3: _____

Words to Preview	**Point & Say**
1 **characteristics** – features that identify a person or thing. *One of the **characteristics** that birds and fish share is that they both lay eggs.*	diamond poisonous
2 **mollusks** – animals with soft bodies but no backbone that often live in shells; most live in the ocean. *Snails, clams, and octopuses are all **mollusks** although they do not all live in shells.*	
3 **cartilage** – a strong, elastic tissue that connects bones in humans and animals. *The top of your outer ear is made out of **cartilage**.*	

Note: Hyphenated words count as one word.

Stingrays

READER 1

Stingrays are interesting animals. They belong to a family of fish called rays.	13
Most rays live in the salt water of the oceans, but some live in the fresh	29
water of rivers.	32
Rays and sharks are in the same group of fish. They have some of the	47
same characteristics. Like sharks, stingrays do not have scales as most fish	59
do. A stingray's skin looks smooth, but it is not. It has little points that face	75
backward. If you rub a stingray back to front, the skin feels like sandpaper.	89
If you rub it front to back, the skin feels smooth and wet.	102

READER 2

Like sharks, stingrays do not have bones. They have a skeleton made	114
of cartilage, which can bend much more easily than bone. This allows	126
stingrays to move faster and make sharper turns.	134

A stingray looks a lot like a kite or a plate with a tail. Some stingrays are   151
shaped like diamonds, but others are round. A stingray's eyes are on the   164
top, and the mouth, nose, and gills are on the bottom.   175

READER 3

The tail of a stingray may be long or short. Either way, it always has a   191
stinger. The stinger is sharp and poisonous. When a stingray is stepped on,   204
its tail flips up and stings. The sting hurts a lot, but it probably will not kill.   221
Sometimes the stinger comes off. When that happens, a new stinger grows   233
back. Stingrays only use their stinger to stay safe, not to get food.   246

Stingrays eat worms and some kinds of shellfish. They use their teeth to   259
break the shells of clams and other mollusks.   267

Stingrays hide while they rest. They dig into the bottom of the sea and hide   282
in the sand. Stingrays often have gray, black, or white spots. Their color   295
helps them hide in the sand.   301

People sometimes step on stingrays that are hiding. To be safe, pull your   314
feet through the sand when you walk on the ocean floor. You will make   328
waves, and the rays will know you are there. They will swim away instead   342
of hurting you.   345

Calculation Boxes

	Reader 1		Reader 2	Reader 3
		Number of Words at Bracket		
		Subtract: Number of Words at Subhead	-102	-175
Number of Words at Bracket		Equals: Number of Words Attempted		
Subtract: Number of Errors	–	Subtract: Number of Errors	–	–
Equals: Words Correct per Minute (WCPM)		Equals: Words Correct per Minute (WCPM)		
Accuracy Percentage	%	Accuracy Percentage	%	%

Mark It!

1. expl<u>ore</u>
2. adore
3. airplane
4. cardboard
5. indoor
6. scoreboard
7. carrot
8. sportsmanship
9. fairly
10. trapdoor
11. ordinary
12. courtside

Read It!

1. explore	ordinary	carrot
2. scoreboard	adore	indoor
3. cardboard	sportsmanship	courtside
4. fairly	airplane	trapdoor
5. ordinary	indoor	cardboard
6. courtside	explore	adore
7. carrot	scoreboard	airplane
8. trapdoor	fairly	sportsmanship

Write each syllable in the correct column. The *schwa* spellings are circled.

CHALLENGING

1. skate•board
2. or•g(a)n
3. north•east
4. b(e)•fore

Closed	Open	VCE	Vowel Team	R-Controlled
		skate		**board**

MORE CHALLENGING

5. bore•d(o)m
6. a•corn
7. up•roar
8. sea•shore

Closed	Open	VCE	Vowel Team	R-Controlled

MOST CHALLENGING

9. car•n(i)•vore
10. court•side
11. fore•cast
12. r(e)•store

Closed	Open	VCE	Vowel Team	R-Controlled

CHALLENGING

1. left a floral vest on my back porch (8)
2. will even the score before the clock runs out (9)
3. cannot repair the trapdoor to the basement (7)
4. did not tip the doorman at the Morgan Hotel (9)

MORE CHALLENGING

5. soar like a condor over the distant cornfields (8)
6. was aware that I ate an artichoke beforehand (8)
7. feel remorse for eating all of the cheesy popcorn (9)
8. can score courtside tickets before the game starts (8)

CHALLENGING

1. Karen is the primary hairstylist at the salon. (8)
2. I am lactose-free, so I have to ignore all dairy. (10)
3. Please do not compare me to the kid next door. (10)
4. Grant wants to explore the seafloor with his yellow snorkel. (10)

MORE CHALLENGING

5. I was stuck at the airport in Arizona for a day before my flight started for New York. (18)
6. Marcus and Arnold are forbidden from eating the assortment of tarts at the store. (14)
7. We slept in the military barracks for an extra night, so I had to bring two pairs of pajamas. (19)
8. The forecast predicts a rainstorm and then a snowstorm, and I predict boredom if I cannot go to the park. (20)

SENTENCES

1. Read each sentence.
2. In Sentence 1, <u>underline</u> all of the spellings of /ār/ as in **air**.
3. In Sentence 2, draw a box around the spellings of /or/ as in **fork**.
4. In Sentence 3, circle the words that contain both the /ār/ and /or/ sounds.

1 While driving through Arizona, I saw a scarecrow wearing a fairy dress.

2 Try to ignore the courtside uproar from the Hornets fans.

3 It is ordinary to wait a short time for your bags in the airport.

CHALLENGE YOURSELF

Using your knowledge of r-controlled vowel spellings, come up with three words that contain each r-controlled vowel phoneme listed below. To make the challenge more difficult, use a different spelling of the r-controlled vowel phoneme in each word. Do not use words from the sentences above.

/ar/   **artist**

     beginning   middle   end

/or/

     beginning   middle   end

Reader 1: _____   Date: _____

Reader 2: _____

Reader 3: _____

Words to Preview	Point & Say
① **tentacles** – long, thin, flexible body parts that stick out around an animal's head or mouth and that are used mainly for feeling or grasping. *All of the **tentacles** on the octopus were moving in different directions.*	climb mollusk
② **suction cups** – small cup-shaped objects that can create a vacuum in order to hold something to a surface. *We had to use **suction cups** to hang our holiday decorations in the windows.*	
③ **sensors** – things that detect sense, such as taste, smell, or touch. *Sensors in our hands allow us to know whether something is hot or cold.*	
④ **detach** – to remove or separate. *Once we got to the campground, we had to **detach** the trailer from the truck.*	

Note: Hyphenated words count as one word.

Octopus

READER 1

An octopus lives in the ocean, but it is not a fish. An octopus has no scales	17
or bones. It is also not a sea mammal. It is a cold-blooded animal. It is a	34
kind of mollusk. There are more than 150 types of octopuses.	45

The word *octopus* means "eight feet." An octopus has eight arms, which	57
are called tentacles. The arms have small suction cups. The suction cups	69
help the octopus open shells, climb, and hold things. Taste sensors in the	82
suction cups help the octopus know what it is touching.	92

READER 2

An octopus spends time hunting for small animals. It searches the sea floor	105
for shellfish such as clams, shrimp, and crabs. After it poisons an animal, the	119
meat gets soft. The octopus eats the meat and throws away the shells. The	133
shells collect in a pile called an "octopus garden." This garden marks the	146
location of the octopus's home.	151

An octopus often crawls, but it swims to move fast. It can move almost as	166
fast as a rabbit. For a short time, octopuses can swim more than 15 miles	181
per hour.	183

READER 3

An octopus has many ways to stay safe. It spends a lot of time hiding in	199
caves under the water. An octopus may also change color to hide. It can	213
change its skin to any color to blend in with the background. It can also	228
make a black cloud of ink so an enemy does not see it get away.	243

To protect itself, an octopus can also detach its own arm. The arm keeps	257
moving and confuses an enemy. The enemy thinks the octopus is still there,	270
so the octopus has time to get away. Later, the octopus grows a new arm.	285

Some octopuses are small, but the giant octopus is very big. A giant	298
octopus can grow to be over 16 feet tall. That's taller than two people	312
combined! The giant octopus does not hurt people. It is a shy animal. It	326
swims away if it sees people or boats. People see many kinds of ocean	340
animals. Not many people are lucky enough to see a giant octopus.	352

Calculation Boxes

Number of Words at Bracket	Reader 1		Reader 2	Reader 3
		Number of Words at Bracket		
		Subtract: Number of Words at Subhead	-92	-183
Number of Words at Bracket		Equals: Number of Words Attempted		
Subtract: Number of Errors	–	Subtract: Number of Errors	–	–
Equals: Words Correct per Minute (WCPM)		Equals: Words Correct per Minute (WCPM)		
Accuracy Percentage	%	Accuracy Percentage	%	%

Mark It!

1. th<u>ir</u>ty
2. person
3. hurtful
4. earthly
5. nocturnal
6. hamburger
7. whirling
8. survive
9. lemur
10. misheard
11. churches
12. squirmy

Read It!

1. person   whirling   squirmy
2. nocturnal   earthly   misheard
3. survive   churches   thirty
4. hurtful   lemur   hamburger
5. whirling   survive   person
6. misheard   thirty   churches
7. lemur   hamburger   nocturnal
8. earthly   squirmy   hurtful

Write each syllable in the correct column. The *schwa* spellings are circled.

CHALLENGING

1. cur•r(e)nt
2. lead•er•ship
3. dir•ect
4. chap•ter

Closed	Open	VCE	Vowel Team	R-Controlled
rent				**cur**

MORE CHALLENGING

5. thir•teen
6. ba•ker•ies
7. Thurs•day
8. yo•gurt

Closed	Open	VCE	Vowel Team	R-Controlled

MOST CHALLENGING

9. u•ser
10. sur•vi•v(a)l
11. r(e)•hear•s(a)l
12. No•vem•ber

Closed	Open	VCE	Vowel Team	R-Controlled

CHALLENGING

1. enter the small kitchen (4)
2. discover a new continent (4)
3. form a partnership for the project (6)
4. perch on a branch with the snowbird (7)

MORE CHALLENGING

5. the shortest show currently on TV at night (8)
6. stay for the winter in western or northern Turkey (9)
7. needs the carpenter's hammer to finish the task (8)
8. held a firsthand report of the nurses helping during a fire (11)

CHALLENGING

1. Can you confirm that you saw a squirrel surfing perfectly? (10)
2. The satellite is not working, so Kirk must take it to the repair store. (14)
3. Albert chose to have a bowling party for his birthday in October. (12)
4. Have you heard the blackbird singing and chirping outside your window? (11)

MORE CHALLENGING

5. Kirk did not understand how Carl could study during rehearsal on Saturday. (12)
6. You were clever to order a hamburger and a milkshake after Fern said she was going to pay. (18)
7. When my throat hurts, my mother takes the thermometer out of the cabinet to see if I am sick. (19)
8. It is much safer to stay away from the turnips that grow under the porch and just eat a pearly white one from the store. (25)

Draw a line to connect the syllables that will spell a real word. Write the whole word on the line.

1. af   turn   **return** _____

    ev   day   _____

    re   ter   _____

    birth   er   _____

2. bor   haps   _____

    mod   nip   _____

    tur   der   _____

    per   ern   _____

3. fur   urb   _____

    sub   gurt   _____

    cur   nish   _____

    yo   rent   _____

4. sur   ther   _____

    squir   vive   _____

    far   form   _____

    per   rel   _____

5. shel   sert   _____

    whirl   ber   _____

    num   ter   _____

    des   wind   _____

6. sear   ter   _____

    purs   teen   _____

    let   es   _____

    thir   ching   _____

CHALLENGE YOURSELF

Using your knowledge of r-controlled vowel spellings, come up with **three** words that contain each r-controlled vowel phoneme listed below. To make the challenge more difficult, use a different spelling of the r-controlled vowel phoneme in each word. Do not use words from above.

1. /or/ _____   _____   _____

2. /er/ _____   _____   _____

Reader 1: _____   Date: _____

Reader 2: _____

Reader 3: _____

Words to Preview | Point & Say

1. **currents** – parts of water that flow in certain directions.
   *The ocean **currents** took the shipwrecked boat far out to sea.*

2. **stuns** – puts in a daze or makes unconscious.
   *The spider's bite **stuns** its prey so that it cannot escape.*

3. **responding** – reacting to something that happens.
   *The boy must be **responding** to the medicine because he stopped coughing.*

4. **venom** – poison that some animals produce to catch prey; usually passed through a sting or bite.
   *The **venom** a snake passes through a bite can be very dangerous to humans.*

Point & Say

jellyfish (jellies)

tentacles

allergic

Note: Hyphenated words count as one word.

Jellyfish

READER 1

A jellyfish is not made of jelly. A jellyfish is not even a fish. Unlike fish, jellyfish	17
have no scales or bones. They do not even have a brain. Jellyfish are mostly	32
made of water, which is why they feel like jelly.	42
Jellyfish, or jellies, live in every ocean. Most live near the top of the water,	57
but a few kinds of jellyfish live in deep water. Jellyfish can swim, but they	72
mostly just float on the water currents. Some jellies do not like light, so they	87
move deeper into the water during the day.	95

READER 2

Jellies come in many sizes and colors. The biggest jellyfish is called a box	109
jellyfish. It can measure over nine feet in length. Most jellies are shaped like	123
a bell and can be any color of the rainbow. Some have no color, which	138
makes them very hard to see.	144

All jellyfish have tentacles that hang down from their bodies. Some	155
tentacles are short, while others are very long. The tentacles have small	167
parts that can sting. The sting puts poison into an animal's body. The poison	181
stuns the animal so that it cannot get away. The jellyfish then traps the	195
animal between its tentacles.	199

READER 3

Jellyfish sting to get food, and they also sting to stay safe. Since they do not	215
have brains, they are not thinking when they sting. They are only responding	228
to the world around them.	233

Some jellyfish are a danger to people. A sting from a small jelly doesn't	247
often cause much pain, but stings from larger jellies can feel like nasty	260
bee stings. Most stings do not kill, but some people are allergic to them.	274
These people can die from a jellyfish sting. A sting from a box jelly is more	290
harmful than snake venom. This kind of sting can kill a person in three	304
minutes. To be safe, people should never get too close to jellyfish. If you do	319
go in water that might have jellyfish, shuffle your feet in the sand so they	334
know to stay away.	338

Calculation Boxes	Reader 1		Reader 2	Reader 3
		Number of Words at Bracket		
		Subtract: Number of Words at Subhead	-95	-199
Number of Words at Bracket		Equals: Number of Words Attempted		
Subtract: Number of Errors	−	Subtract: Number of Errors	−	−
Equals: Words Correct per Minute (WCPM)		Equals: Words Correct per Minute (WCPM)		
Accuracy Percentage	%	Accuracy Percentage	%	%

Mark It!

1. calend<u>ar</u>
2. motor
3. calculator
4. mustard
5. nectar
6. predator

7. wordy
8. projector
9. factory
10. grammar
11. cheddar
12. afterward

Read It!

1. calendar　　　nectar　　　afterward
2. factory　　　motor　　　calculator
3. mustard　　　grammar　　　predator
4. cheddar　　　wordy　　　projector
5. calculator　　　calendar　　　motor
6. grammar　　　mustard　　　factory
7. predator　　　projector　　　wordy
8. nectar　　　afterward　　　cheddar

▶ Word Sort

Write the spelling of the r-controlled phonemes in the correct column. The *schwa* spellings are circled.

CHALLENGING

1. al•li•ga•tor
2. or•chard
3. mar•ching
4. for•ward

/ar/ as in barn	/or/ as in fork	/er/ as in bird
		or

MORE CHALLENGING

5. nor•mal
6. col•lec•tor
7. world•ly
8. a•part•ment

/ar/ as in barn	/or/ as in fork	/er/ as in bird

MOST CHALLENGING

9. in•ven•tor
10. im•por•tant
11. pop•u•lar
12. score•card

/ar/ as in barn	/or/ as in fork	/er/ as in bird

CHALLENGING

1. was a collector of stellar art (6)

2. victory was not as important (5)

3. in the orchard or the cornfield (6)

4. is a wizard at perfect grammar (6)

MORE CHALLENGING

5. has a working tractor on his chicken farm (8)

6. ate artichokes with the popular armadillo (6)

7. heard chirping in the darkness by the pillar (8)

8. before the normal visitors arrive at the bookstore (8)

CHALLENGING

1. I want to earn fifty dollars to donate to the church in Corning. (13)

2. Can you please find aspirin for Connor and then monitor him? (11)

3. Clifford prefers to mix his collard greens with cheddar and mustard. (11)

4. Dora's shirt collar was torn on a sharp branch when she hid in the orchard. (15)

MORE CHALLENGING

5. Edward the earthworm chose to bravely enter the winter blizzard in his yellow parka. (14)

6. Mara will pick a carpet color to match the cardinal that perches on her windowsill. (15)

7. Before Margo went soaring off to Bora Bora, she had to search for her thermometer. (15)

8. Mark, my brother, is a bowler, an actor, an artist, a soccer player, and a member of the gardening club. (20)

Word Hunt

1. Read each word.
2. Underline the spelling **ar** when it spells the sound /er/.
3. Draw a box around the spelling **or** when it spells the sound /er/.
4. Circle words that have three or more syllables.

blizzard	adore	ambassador
collector	backward	organize
artichoke	flavor	earthworm
grammar	hazard	harbor
instructor	popular	border

CHALLENGE YOURSELF

1. Find 3 words that are careers.

_____ _____ _____

2. Find the word that means "love."_____

3. Find a word that might be on a menu. _____

4. Find the word that is a type of storm. _____

© 2015 Really Great Reading Company, LLC **89**

Reader 1: _____   Date: _____

Reader 2: _____

Reader 3: _____

Words to Preview	Point & Say

1   **lever** – a handle used to adjust or operate a machine.
Push the lever to the left to start the machine.

2   **invented** – created, or made.
Alexander Graham Bell invented the telephone.

3   **assembly line** – a process in which finished products are made in an efficient manner.
Building cars on an assembly line made it faster to produce cars.

4   **puncture** – to create a small hole.
A nail can puncture a car's tires, which will make them go flat.

Point & Say:
accidents
station

Note: Hyphenated words count as one word.

Cars

READER 1

Long ago, there were no cars. People used horses, trains, or boats to make	14
long trips. A man invented the first car with a motor in 1885. His car had	30
three wheels and a long seat with the motor behind the seat. The car had	45
a lever to turn the car instead of a steering wheel. Another lever stopped	59
the car.	61
Henry Ford made some of the first American cars. In 1908, his company	74
sold a new kind of car called the Model T. He used an assembly line to	90
build this car.	93

READER 2

The assembly line helped people build cars faster. It also made cars cost	106
less to make. Since cars cost less to make, they also cost less to buy. More	122
people could buy cars because of this.	129

When cars were first invented, there were many accidents on the roads. | 141
This is because people used different types of transportation. Not everyone | 152
drove a car. Some people traveled by walking, by horse, or in horse pulled | 166
buggies. Now, cars were on the roads with them. People on foot and on | 180
horses were scared of the cars. Accidents happened when horses jumped | 191
at the car noises. | 195

READER 3

People were not always careful when they drove. There were also no traffic | 208
signals or stop signs long ago. Some people would not watch where they | 221
were going, and they would get into accidents. New York had a special | 234
law until 1901 that said a man had to walk in front of every car. He waved | 251
a red flag to let people know that a car was coming. This would help keep | 267
people safe. | 269

People who owned early cars had other problems. Gas stations were not | 281
common, and they did not always have much gas. Also, tires were not | 294
strong. Most roads were just made of dirt. Stones would puncture tires, and | 307
flat tires were hard to change. | 313

The first cars did not move fast. Today, cars can move very fast. A jet car | 329
moves faster than anything on land. It can move faster than some airplanes | 342
can fly. Even though you can drive a car fast, make sure to follow the speed | 358
limit. You want to be safe and not get into an accident! | 370

Calculation Boxes

Number of Words at Bracket	Reader 1		Reader 2	Reader 3
		Number of Words at Bracket		
		Subtract: Number of Words at Subhead	-78	-165
Number of Words at Bracket		Equals: Number of Words Attempted		
Subtract: Number of Errors	–	Subtract: Number of Errors	–	–
Equals: Words Correct per Minute (WCPM)		Equals: Words Correct per Minute (WCPM)		
Accuracy Percentage	%	Accuracy Percentage	%	%

Mark It!

1. n<u>ew</u>spaper
2. conclude
3. dewdrop
4. bedroom
5. unscrew
6. fireproof
7. cartoonist
8. student
9. loosen
10. igloo
11. rumor
12. salute

Read It!

1. conclude
2. student
3. unscrew
4. rumor
5. fireproof
6. cartoonist
7. dewdrop
8. bedroom

bedroom
cartoonist
igloo
dewdrop
unscrew
newspaper
salute
loosen

loosen
fireproof
newspaper
salute
conclude
rumor
igloo
student

Place a checkmark in the correct column for the spelling of /o͞o/ as in **ooze**. The *schwa* spellings are circled.

CHALLENGING

1. grew
2. in•clude
3. rac•coon
4. truth•f(u)l

oo	u_e	ew	u
		✓	

MORE CHALLENGING

5. to•fu
6. bloom
7. af•ter•noon
8. flute

oo	u_e	ew	u

MOST CHALLENGING

9. at•t(i)•tude
10. su•per•he•ro
11. c(a)•boo•s(e)s
12. jew•(e)l•ry

oo	u_e	ew	u

CHALLENGING

1. can smooch the African baboon (5)

2. felt gratitude for the cool new hoopskirt (7)

3. plays soothing flute music on the record (7)

4. lost a tooth while snoozing in the living room (9)

MORE CHALLENGING

5. sat on a toadstool to read the student newspaper (9)

6. ate a maroon gluten-free macaroon with her coffee (8)

7. form an afternoon carpool between here and Liverpool (8)

8. saw a toothless duck in the shallow and overgrown lagoon (10)

CHALLENGING

1. Sue has too many toothbrushes and loofas in her bathroom. (10)

2. Rudy, when brewing tea, remember to turn the burner off afterwards. (11)

3. Snoopy sat in solitude in the stateroom, spooling string onto the spoon rest. (13)

4. The superb afternoon sun played peek-a-boo with the yellowwood treetops. (10)

MORE CHALLENGING

5. The toothless crusader has to slurp down slimy prunes, tuna, bamboo shoots, and mushrooms. (14)

6. It is rude to intrude while I am rehearsing the Chattanooga Choo Choo on my bassoon in my bedroom! (19)

7. Juniper wanted to win the hula hoop contest, but she kept a positive attitude when she fell and withdrew. (19)

8. Every morning, Ruby the rooster perches on the rooftop to yodel "cock-a-doodle-doo" and wake the snoozing farmer and all of the animals. (22)

SENTENCES

1. Read each sentence.
2. In Sentence 1, <u>underline</u> the words that have the /o͞o/ sound spelled with the letters you see in the word **drew**.
3. In Sentence 2, draw a box around all words that include the /o͞o/ sound.
4. In Sentence 3, circle the words that rhyme with the word **too**.

1. Andrew and his crew have to look in the newspaper for summer jobs.

2. The students in my carpool consume chewy mushrooms every afternoon.

3. I had to shoo the animals in the zoo back to their homes to eat their dinner of stew so they did not get the flu.

CHALLENGE YOURSELF

Circle the correct vowel sound for each word. You may need to say each word aloud to hear the vowel sound correctly.

1. cute /yo͞o/ or /o͞o/

2. rude /yo͞o/ or /o͞o/

3. pupil /yo͞o/ or /o͞o/

4. tuna /yo͞o/ or /o͞o/

5. prune /yo͞o/ or /o͞o/

6. human /yo͞o/ or /o͞o/

7. user /yo͞o/ or /o͞o/

8. numeral /yo͞o/ or /o͞o/

9. argument /yo͞o/ or /o͞o/

10. consume /yo͞o/ or /o͞o/

Reader 1: _____ Date: _____

Reader 2: _____

Reader 3: _____

Words to Preview	Point & Say
1 **diesel** – oil-based fuel that is thicker and heavier than gasoline. *Diesel is a type of fuel used in some cars that do not use an electric spark to start their engines.*	engine
2 **locomotive** – an engine used to push or pull railroad cars. *The locomotive pushed the train along the track.*	electric
3 **engineer** – a person who works with engines and other machines. *The engineer helped keep the train's engine running smoothly.*	countries
4 **pollution** – things that are harmful to the Earth. *Pollution in the water can hurt or kill things that live in the ocean.*	

Note: Hyphenated words count as one word.

Trains

READER 1

Trains run on rails. They get power from locomotives, or engines.	11
The locomotives push or pull trains along a track. Some trains are so	24
heavy that they have to use more than one engine to move.	36
Long ago, before engines were invented, horses pulled trains along tracks.	47
Then, about 300 years ago, an engineer made the first steam engine.	59
Steam engines worked better than horses. Engines have much more power	70
than horses, so they can move heavy loads over mountains. They can also	83
move much faster than horses. Trains with steam engines can travel	94
100 miles an hour.	98

READER 2

Trains with steam engines take a long time to start. First, a fire is made in a	115
special box. Water in a large tank gets very hot, and the water turns into	130
steam. Then the engineer can start the locomotive. It takes about three	142
hours to make enough steam to start the train.	151

Few trains run on steam these days. Now, most have diesel or electric	164
engines. Diesel engines can go farther than electric ones without needing	175
more fuel. However, not everything about diesel engines is better.	185

READER 3

When diesel burns, it makes black smoke, smells bad, and creates pollution.	197
Electric engines are much cleaner, but it costs more to make electric trains.	210

The fastest trains in the world are electric. Many countries have electric	222
trains. One train in China travels at 430 miles an hour!	233

Monorails are trains that run on only one rail instead of on two. The prefix	248
mono means "one." The word *monorail* means "one rail." Many cities	259
around the world have monorails. They run on rails above streets, on land,	272
and under the ground.	276

People like to look at and take pictures of trains. Some people even take	290
trips to see different kinds of trains. Today, people use trains to travel and	304
see different places. Trains have places to eat and sleep inside the train.	317
Some trains even have showers!	322

Calculation Boxes

	Reader 1		Reader 2	Reader 3
		Number of Words at Bracket		
		Subtract: Number of Words at Subhead	-78	-165
Number of Words at Bracket		Equals: Number of Words Attempted		
Subtract: Number of Errors	–	Subtract: Number of Errors	–	–
Equals: Words Correct per Minute (WCPM)		Equals: Words Correct per Minute (WCPM)		
Accuracy Percentage	%	Accuracy Percentage	%	%

Mark It!

1. destr<u>oy</u>
2. boyish
3. loyal
4. annoy
5. jointed
6. enjoy
7. poison
8. royalty
9. boiling
10. appointment
11. oyster
12. noisy

Read It!

1. boyish	loyal	appointment
2. noisy	enjoy	destroy
3. royalty	poison	boiling
4. annoy	jointed	oyster
5. poison	appointment	boyish
6. destroy	noisy	enjoy
7. jointed	boiling	annoy
8. loyal	oyster	royalty

Write all vowel spellings in the correct columns. The *schwa* spellings are circled and filled in.

CHALLENGING

1. grat•i•tude
2. a•void
3. tea•spoon
4. voy•age

Short	Long	R-Controlled	Other	Schwa
a			u_e	i
				a
				a_e

MORE CHALLENGING

5. ru•by
6. em•ploy•ee
7. pin•point
8. ar•gu•ment

Short	Long	R-Controlled	Other	Schwa
				e
				e

MOST CHALLENGING

9. o•ver•joy
10. shal•low•ness
11. dis•ap•point
12. truth•ful•ly

Short	Long	R-Controlled	Other	Schwa
				e
				a
				u

CHALLENGING

1. ate a moist pork loin for dinner (7)

2. can be a batboy for the last game (8)

3. made a toy rooster out of corduroy (7)

4. spoonful of oily soybean and raccoon stew (7)

MORE CHALLENGING

5. will try to avoid the noisy voyage to Detroit (9)

6. newsboy left the paper on the steps of our porch (10)

7. might be disappointed by the game's broken joystick (8)

8. pointed to the poster of the royal family and the loyal Yorkie (12)

CHALLENGING

1. Bring the stew to a boil and broil the meat in oil. (12)

2. Joy avoided the pool when the noisy children were in it. (11)

3. Farmer Roy fed the annoying pigs soybeans to keep them from oinking. (12)

4. Moira needed more ointment for the itchy poison ivy on her arms and legs. (14)

MORE CHALLENGING

5. Troy was the poster boy for a topsoil company in Chattanooga, Tennessee. (12)

6. The boys enjoy making mud cakes from the moist soil until they hear Mom shriek. (15)

7. The boy had a doctor's appointment that he was trying to avoid by pretending to be fine. (17)

8. Floyd put a decoy duck in the pond to dupe, or trick, the annoying bobcat that kept chasing the real ones. (21)

Add **oi** or **oy** to finish the incomplete words in each sentence. Write the whole word on the line.

1. My little sister does her best to ann____ me. _____

2. The paperb____ keeps throwing our paper in the wet grass. _____

3. Please make the n____sy dogs stop barking. _____

4. It is best to av____d the traffic jam. _____

5. Did your hamster destr____ his spinning wheel? _____

6. How many c____ns do you have left in your piggy bank? _____

7. Tim wore cordur____ pants. _____

8. Snake venom is a kind of p____son. _____

9. Do you enj____ visits with your grandmother? _____

10. The baby p____nted to the colorful ball. _____

11. The pirate said, "Ah____, matey!" _____

12. Please b____l the carrots for dinner. _____

13. The busb____ clears the dinner dishes away. _____

14. Put a thin layer of ____ntment on the burn. _____

15. Br____l the fish for our brunch. _____

CHALLENGE YOURSELF

Try to figure out the correct spelling of /oi/ in each of these challenge words.

1. ____ster   2. r____al   3. t____let

4. v____age   5. ____ly   6. j____ful

Reader 1: _____   Date: _____

Reader 2: _____

Reader 3: _____

Words to Preview	**Point & Say**

1. **paddle wheel** – a wheel with boards that rotates to move a boat.
   *Steam helps turn the **paddle wheel** of the fancy riverboat as it travels down the Mississippi River.*

2. **barge** – a flat-bottomed boat that moves cargo or people.
   *Many **barges** travel up and down the Mississippi River.*

3. **defense** – protection.
   *Many people learn karate for **defense**.*

4. **explore** – to travel in search of something.
   *The children **explored** the forest to see what they could find.*

Point & Say

sightseeing

canoes

helicopter

Note: Hyphenated words count as one word.

Boats

READER 1

Land covers less than one-third of the Earth. Water covers the rest. Long   13
ago, there were no trains, planes, or cars. People used boats and ships to   27
go places. They explored the world by boat. People also used boats and   40
ships for fun, work, and defense. We use boats for the same reasons today.   54

Large boats can carry many people on long, wide rivers. Some of these   67
boats have a big paddle wheel on the back. The wheel has twelve   80
paddles. The paddle wheel turns and pushes the water. This makes the   92
boat move.   94

READER 2

Boats that take people on sightseeing trips have places to eat, sleep, swim, 107
and dance on the boat. Some trips are just a few hours, but others are a   123
week or more.   126

Barges are another kind of boat. They are long and flat and have to be 141
pushed by a towboat. They travel on canals, lakes, and rivers, and they 154
carry cargo from one port to another. Cargo is goods that are being 167
transported from one place to another. Some barges carry large boxes 178
of furniture or clothes. Others carry coal or stone. Some barges carry cars 191
made in other countries. 195

READER 3

Canoes are small boats used on rivers and lakes. They are easy to paddle 209
by hand. Long ago, canoes were made from tree trunks, but today most 222
are made from plastic or metal. 228

Motorboats and sailboats are used on rivers, lakes, bays, and oceans. 239
People use motorboats to water-ski and to fish. Sailboats are fun to race 252
when the wind blows. People also use them for quiet trips. 263

Very large ships are used on oceans. They may carry wood, oil, or cars. 277
Others carry people. Some move airplanes, helicopters, and sailors. 286
They need to be strong to carry heavy cargo. 295

People use boats for many reasons. Some are used for fun. Some are for 309
relaxing. Some carry cargo from port to port. Others are used to keep 322
people, coasts, and our country safe. 328

Calculation Boxes

	Reader 1		Reader 2	Reader 3
		Number of Words at Bracket		
		Subtract: Number of Words at Subhead	-94	-195
Number of Words at Bracket		Equals: Number of Words Attempted		
Subtract: Number of Errors	–	Subtract: Number of Errors	–	–
Equals: Words Correct per Minute (WCPM)		Equals: Words Correct per Minute (WCPM)		
Accuracy Percentage	%	Accuracy Percentage	%	%

Mark It!

1. acc<u>ou</u>nt
2. frowning
3. proudest
4. sprouted
5. discount
6. coward
7. flourless
8. around
9. growling
10. however
11. flower
12. cloudy

Read It!

1. frowning	account	around
2. cloudy	sprouted	coward
3. proudest	growling	however
4. flourless	discount	flower
5. account	however	cloudy
6. sprouted	coward	proudest
7. growling	around	flourless
8. flower	frowning	discount

Write all vowel spellings in the correct columns. The *schwa* spellings are circled and filled in.

CHALLENGING

1. thou•s(a)nd
2. fool•ish•ly
3. with•out
4. car•pool

Short	Long	R-Controlled	Other	Schwa
			ou	a

MORE CHALLENGING

5. (a)•round
6. back•ground
7. pow•der
8. check•point

Short	Long	R-Controlled	Other	Schwa
				a

MOST CHALLENGING

9. (e)n•coun•ter
10. loy•(a)l•ties
11. sun•flow•er
12. al•(i)•ga•tor

Short	Long	R-Controlled	Other	Schwa
				e
				a
				i

CHALLENGING

1. has to learn to ask without pouting (7)
2. wore a crown made out of bath towels (8)
3. wants to catch a bigmouth bass or a trout (9)
4. look for stars in the south on a cloudless night (10)

MORE CHALLENGING

5. is afraid to encounter a slimy, round earthworm (8)
6. flew to the ground in search of the nut-brown owl (10)
7. thousands of yellow sunflowers sprouted in the field (8)
8. vows to bake a flourless chocolate cake for the cowgirl (10)

CHALLENGING

1. The baby frowns each time the shaggy brown dog growls. (10)
2. The rowdy crowd shouted loudly after the thrilling final play. (10)
3. The townsmen needed to shut down the south tower for repairs. (11)
4. When trying to read a complicated word, look for the vowels first. (12)

MORE CHALLENGING

5. The cashier will take the discount for that item off at the checkout counter. (14)
6. Wow, the starflowers on the carnival fairgrounds are surprisingly impressive! (10)
7. During the estate sale, the brownstone was so crowded that I had to wait outside. (15)
8. We are relocating to South Carolina this summer, so I have to scout out new housing. (16)

SENTENCES

1. Read each sentence.
2. <u>Underline</u> the words that have the /ou/ sound spelled with the letters you see in the word **ouch**.
3. Circle the words that have the /ou/ sound spelled with the letters you see in the word **cow**.
4. Draw a box around words with the **ow** spelling that does not make the /ou/ sound.

1. After a thunderstorm, a colorful rainbow can appear in the clouds on the horizon.

2. J's Oyster Bar in Allentown has the absolute best bowl of seafood chowder.

3. Beans and Brussels sprouts are good side dishes to have with cowboy chicken.

CHALLENGE YOURSELF

Read each clue and write the answer on the line. Every answer will be only one word, and that word will include one of the spellings of /ou/.

1. I fly at night and can turn my neck all the way around. _____

2. I help you to speak and to eat. _____

3. I am colorful, and bees like me. _____

4. I can dry something that is wet. _____

5. I am a person or a thing. _____

Reader 1: _____ Date: _____

Reader 2: _____

Reader 3: _____

Words to Preview	Point & Say
1 **reacts** – acts in response to something else. *When I step on the brakes, the car reacts by slowing down.*	tailwind
2 **current** – a large portion of air or water that flows in one direction. *The strong wind current blew all the papers down the street.*	headwind
3 **skilled** – having the ability to perform a task well because of training and practice. *The skilled pilot landed the plane safely in the field.*	crosswind
4 **destination** – a place to which someone or something is going. *Once we knew our final destination, we could figure out the best route.*	

Note: Hyphenated words count as one word.

Pilots

READER 1

Airplane pilots must know all about the wind. They need to be aware of	14
both wind speed and wind direction when they fly. They must know how	27
the force of the wind impacts their plane. They must take the correct	40
actions when their plane reacts to the wind.	48

It is important for pilots to understand the jet stream. The jet stream is not a	64
jet or a body of water. It is a fast, wavy current of wind that flows about six	82
to nine miles above the Earth. The jet stream is located between the cold	96
air from the north and the warm air from the south.	107

READER 2

The jet stream usually moves around the Earth from the west to the east.	121
Pilots like to fly in the jet stream from west to east. The jet stream will push the	139
plane along quickly. However, pilots flying from east to west try to stay out of	154
the jet stream. That is because the jet stream could slow down the plane.	168

A tailwind is a wind that is moving in the same direction as the plane. Skilled   184
pilots make good use of a tailwind. They let the tailwind do the work to push   200
the plane along. This saves time and fuel.   208

READER 3

A headwind is a wind that flows in the opposite direction the plane is flying.   223
A headwind slows the plane down. A plane slows down more when the   236
headwind is faster. A plane fighting a headwind may need extra time to   249
reach its destination. It also may need extra fuel.   258

Headwinds can also help airplane pilots. Planes must slow down as they   270
approach the airport. A headwind helps to slow the plane for landing. If   283
possible, pilots steer directly into a headwind for landing.   292

A crosswind is a wind that flows across a plane from the side. Crosswinds   306
make it very tricky for a plane to take off or land. Pilots must know how to   323
take off and land safely when crosswinds are blowing.   332

Wise pilots understand the jet stream, headwinds, tailwinds, and crosswinds.   342
This allows them to make excellent use of wind speed and wind direction.   355

Calculation Boxes	Reader 1		Reader 2	Reader 3
		Number of Words at Bracket		
		Subtract: Number of Words at Subhead	-107	-208
Number of Words at Bracket		Equals: Number of Words Attempted		
Subtract: Number of Errors	–	Subtract: Number of Errors	–	–
Equals: Words Correct per Minute (WCPM)		Equals: Words Correct per Minute (WCPM)		
Accuracy Percentage	%	Accuracy Percentage	%	%

Mark It!

1. b <u>oo</u> k l e t
2. r o o k i e
3. f u l l n e s s
4. s k e t c h b o o k
5. w o o d s h e d
6. c o o k i n g
7. w o r k b o o k
8. f o o t p r i n t
9. t e x t b o o k
10. m i s u n d e r s t o o d
11. p u s h c a r t
12. u n d e r t o o k

Read It!

1. fullness	misunderstood	rookie
2. undertook	sketchbook	footprint
3. woodshed	booklet	textbook
4. workbook	pushcart	cooking
5. sketchbook	woodshed	workbook
6. textbook	rookie	booklet
7. misunderstood	cooking	pushcart
8. footprint	fullness	undertook

Word Sort

Write all vowel spellings in the correct columns. The *schwa* spellings are circled and filled in.

CHALLENGING

1. o•ver•look
2. flow•er
3. cook•ie
4. bru•t(a)l

Short	Long	R-Controlled	Other	Schwa
	o	er	oo	
				a

MORE CHALLENGING

5. book•worm
6. look•(a)•like
7. push•cart
8. un•der•cook

Short	Long	R-Controlled	Other	Schwa
				a

MOST CHALLENGING

9. book•keep•er
10. sis•ter•hood
11. ex•ter•n(a)l
12. trap•(e)•zoid

Short	Long	R-Controlled	Other	Schwa
				a
				e

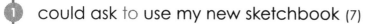

CHALLENGING

1. could ask to use my new sketchbook (7)

2. retook the history test yesterday morning (6)

3. made a bookmark out of a thin strip of wood (10)

4. will put a fishhook on the line to catch the rainbow trout (12)

MORE CHALLENGING

5. cannot play football until her homework is complete (8)

6. are staying at the ranch overlooking Rockwood Lake (8)

7. got really good footage of Roy and Ruby in Hollywood (10)

8. crook took my pocketbook full of cash and my best camera (11)

CHALLENGING

1. Let's sit under this redwood tree for a delightful cookout. (10)

2. "Please save a peanut butter cookie for me!" said Mister Wood. (11)

3. Brooks felt foolish after he mistook Oliver's wool pullover for his own. (12)

4. June, my classmate, should really have the nickname "bookworm." (9)

MORE CHALLENGING

5. While on our hike in Sherwood Forest, we saw woodchuck footprints beside deer hoof prints. (15)

6. Dagwood made a bookcase out of driftwood he found near the footbridge by the small pond. (16)

7. The red drops on the actor's bandage were made from chocolate pudding, so they did not scare me. (18)

8. Before reading the entire handbook, Emerson wanted to skim it to look for rules about cooking outdoors. (17)

WORDS

1. Read each word.
2. Underline words that contain the /o͝o/ sound, as in **book**.
3. Draw a box around words that contain the /o͞o/ sound, as in **ooze**.
4. Circle words that contain the /yo͞o/ sound, as in **cute**.

bloom	pudding	humid
checkbook	flu	exclude
absolute	onlooker	woodchuck
pushcart	music	hula
typhoon	duty	misunderstood

CHALLENGE YOURSELF

1. Find the word that is a living creature. _____

2. Find the word that means "to leave out." _____

3. Find 2 words that have to do with weather.

_____   _____

4. Find the word that is something someone has to do. _____

Reader 1: _____   Date: _____

Reader 2: _____

Reader 3: _____

Words to Preview   Point & Say

1. **windsock** – a fabric tube that hangs from a pole, used to tell the direction the wind is blowing.
   *The **windsock** shows the wind is blowing from the south right now.*

2. **skipper** – the captain of a boat or ship.
   *The **skipper** is responsible for everyone's safety on a boat.*

3. **rudder** – a flat, movable blade at the back of a boat used to control the boat's direction.
   *We could not turn the boat around after the **rudder** hit a rock and broke.*

4. **exposed** – put out in the open.
   *When they pulled off the cover, a beautiful painting was **exposed**.*

destination

angle

tailwind

Note: Hyphenated words count as one word.

Sailors

READER 1

Sailors both respect and fear the wind. The right winds can help sailors   13
safely reach their destination. Harsh winds can destroy a sailboat. Weak   24
winds can bring a sailboat to a stop.   32

Wind is the force that powers a sailboat. Good sailors understand wind   44
direction. They often fly a flag or windsock to learn the direction of   57
the wind.   59

Winds are named for the direction they are blowing from. That means that   72
a wind blowing from the south to the north is called a south wind. A wind   88
blowing from the west to east is called a west wind.   99

READER 2

Sailing is easiest when the sailboat is headed in the same direction as the	113
wind. This is called a tailwind. The tailwind fills the sail so the boat moves	128
smoothly across the water. The sailboat will go fastest when the skipper puts	141
the sails fully up to catch the wind.	149

It is not as easy to sail against the wind. To head into the wind, the boat	166
must sail in a zigzag pattern. This is called tacking. To tack, the skipper steers	181
the boat at an angle against the wind. After a while, the skipper turns the	196
boat and sails at a different angle. Tacking lets the sailboat stay on course	210
when sailing against the wind.	215

READER 3

Too much wind can be bad for the sail. The wind forces the sailboat to lean	231
over on its side. When a boat leans too much, the rudder cannot work right.	246
The skipper may not be able to steer the boat. Sometimes too much wind in	261
the sails makes a boat tip over into the water.	271

A sailboat's skipper and crew are always on the lookout for strong winds.	284
Strong winds can damage a boat in many ways. They can shred the sails	298
on a boat. They might even rip the steel cables from the mast. The mast is	314
the tall pole that holds up the sails. When that happens, the mast falls and	329
the sails end up in the water.	336

When the wind is too strong, a wise skipper will make the sail smaller. That	351
means less of the sail is exposed to the wind. Doing this makes the boat	366
more stable. Sometimes the crew will even take down all the sails. The wind	380
will not do as much damage when the sails are down.	391

Calculation Boxes

	Reader 1		Reader 2	Reader 3
		Number of Words at Bracket		
		Subtract: Number of Words at Subhead	-99	-215
Number of Words at Bracket		Equals: Number of Words Attempted		
Subtract: Number of Errors	–	Subtract: Number of Errors	–	–
Equals: Words Correct per Minute (WCPM)		Equals: Words Correct per Minute (WCPM)		
Accuracy Percentage	%	Accuracy Percentage	%	%

Mark It!

1. p<u>a</u>using
2. August
3. launching
4. seesaw
5. cauliflower
6. crawling
7. haunted
8. awful
9. drawback
10. applaud
11. squawking
12. flawless

Read It!

1. August   pausing   seesaw
2. launching   applaud   flawless
3. crawling   drawback   cauliflower
4. squawking   awful   haunted
5. flawless   crawling   pausing
6. seesaw   launching   drawback
7. applaud   cauliflower   squawking
8. haunted   August   awful

Write each syllable in the correct column. The *schwa* spellings are circled.

CHALLENGING

1. jig•saw
2. foot•note
3. raw•hide
4. chew•y

Closed	Open	VCE	Vowel Team	R-Controlled
jig			saw	

MORE CHALLENGING

5. laun•dry
6. cow•ard
7. chim•ney
8. de•claw

Closed	Open	VCE	Vowel Team	R-Controlled

MOST CHALLENGING

9. awk•ward
10. au•t(o)•graph
11. (a)•part•m(e)nt
12. foot•lock•er

Closed	Open	VCE	Vowel Team	R-Controlled

CHALLENGING

1. yawning at dawn after no sleep (6)
2. will use a jigsaw to fix the awful mess (9)
3. crawling on the ground like a toddler (7)
4. can launch a small stone off of the seesaw (9)

MORE CHALLENGING

5. did not enjoy visiting the scrawny Santa Claus (8)
6. can broil some cauliflower and carrots for dinner (8)
7. had an outdoor picnic on the lawn at the end of August (12)
8. has drawn a newborn fawn in the woods in her notebook (11)

CHALLENGING

1. Did you see Dawson crawling to pick up the blue straws? (11)
2. Saul, do you go to haunted houses or go on hayrides in October? (13)
3. Paula had to thaw the frozen sausage for supper before cooking it. (12)
4. Mister Paws, Shaun's pet dog, likes to chew rawhide with his big jaws. (13)

MORE CHALLENGING

5. Even if Shawn's vault is not flawless, you should applaud, not gawk at her. (14)
6. Aubrey took Dawn for an authentic prawn dinner last night for her birthday. (12)
7. What is causing that awful odor that is oozing out from under your bedroom door? (15)
8. Austin has to sort his laundry, mow the lawn, and fix the flaw in his art project before he can go to the carnival. (24)

Draw a line to connect the syllables that will spell a real word. Write the whole word on the line.

1. see   dry   **laundry**

   au   sing   _____

   pau   saw   _____

   laun   thor   _____

2. aw   draw   _____

   flaw   ful   _____

   with   a   _____

   saun   less   _____

3. cole   ing   _____

   crawl   ward   _____

   awk   fish   _____

   craw   slaw   _____

4. chain   gust   _____

   Au   ted   _____

   saw   saw   _____

   haun   dust   _____

CHALLENGE YOURSELF

Choose **two** words from above, and write **one** sentence that includes both of those words on the lines below.

_____

_____

Choose **two** different words from above, and write **one** sentence that includes both of those words on the lines below.

_____

_____

Reader 1: _____   Date: _____

Reader 2: _____

Reader 3: _____

Words to Preview	Point & Say

1 **upwind** – against the direction the wind is coming from.
*To avoid breathing smoke, stand **upwind** from a fire.*

2 **downwind** – in the direction that the wind is blowing.
*If you stand **downwind** from a wildfire, you are sure to breathe in lots of smoke.*

oxygen

create

fuel

Note: Hyphenated words count as one word.

Firefighters

READER 1

Some outdoor fires spread quickly. They are called wildfires. Firefighters   10
have a hard time containing wildfires when the wind changes direction or   22
picks up speed.   25

Wildfires happen in places with many trees or lots of dry grass. People who   39
live in these areas need to watch for signs of fire. The most common sign of   55
fire is smoke.   58

A fire needs three things in order to burn. It needs fuel, heat, and oxygen.   73
For a wildfire, the fuel comes from plants and trees. Dried leaves and twigs   87
on the ground are also fuel for wildfires.   95

READER 2

The heat usually comes from a spark or a flame. Sometimes lightning strikes   108
and starts a fire. People who live where wildfires can happen need to be   122
careful when they use tools that create a flame or spark. These include   135
lighters, grills, lawn mowers, or leaf blowers.   142

Oxygen is the final thing a fire needs. Oxygen is in the air. Strong winds	157
provide a fire with a great deal of oxygen.	166
Wind is a powerful force of nature that causes wildfires to spread quickly.	179
On a windy day, fire quickly leaps from place to place. The faster the wind,	194
the faster the fire spreads. It is much easier for firefighters to put out a fire	210
on a day with little or no wind. In windy weather, the fire chief must call for	227
extra firefighters to stop a fire.	232

READER 3

Firefighters use the direction of the wind to help them fight fire. They try to	247
stay upwind from a fire. Upwind is the direction the wind is coming from.	261
When firefighters stay upwind, they can keep away from smoke and flames.	273
Downwind is the direction the wind is blowing. Firefighters spray water	284
downwind into the flames. The wind carries the water to the fire. If the	298
firefighters sprayed water upwind, it would blow right back in their faces.	310
Firefighters also use wind direction to help find fires. When they see smoke in	324
the sky, they note which way the wind is blowing. Wind carries smoke away	338
from the fire. Firefighters can follow the smoke toward the fire.	349
Even when the weather is not windy, a fire can still spread quickly. That	363
is because a wildfire can create its own wind. When the air above the	377
fire gets hotter, it rises. As it rises, cooler air rushes in to replace it. This air	394
movement creates wind and helps the fire spread.	402

Calculation Boxes

	Reader 1		Reader 2	Reader 3
		Number of Words at Bracket		
		Subtract: Number of Words at Subhead	-95	-232
		Equals: Number of Words Attempted		
Number of Words at Bracket				
Subtract: Number of Errors	−	Subtract: Number of Errors	−	−
Equals: Words Correct per Minute (WCPM)		Equals: Words Correct per Minute (WCPM)		
Accuracy Percentage	%	Accuracy Percentage	%	%

Mark It!

1. fl <u>aw</u> less
2. absolute
3. bookworm
4. noisily
5. brownies
6. download
7. applaud
8. drowsy
9. joyfully
10. goodwill
11. pudding
12. cartoon

Read It!

1. noisily
2. brownies
3. joyfully
4. download
5. cartoon
6. bookworm
7. drowsy
8. goodwill

pudding
cartoon
absolute
applaud
joyfully
brownies
flawless
noisily

bookworm
drowsy
goodwill
flawless
pudding
download
applaud
absolute

Write the spelling for each "other" vowel phoneme. The *schwa* spellings are circled.

CHALLENGING

1. com•pound
2. Au•g(u)st
3. poi•s(o)n
4. car•pool

/o͞o/ as in ooze	/oi/ as in oink	/ou/ as in ouch	/o͝o/ as in book	/aw/ as in awesome
		ou		

MORE CHALLENGING

5. cook•ware
6. (e)n•joy•m(e)nt
7. down•pour
8. chain•saw

/o͞o/ as in ooze	/oi/ as in oink	/ou/ as in ouch	/o͝o/ as in book	/aw/ as in awesome

MOST CHALLENGING

9. boun•d(a)•ry
10. c(o)n•clu•ding
11. push•cart
12. o•ver•threw

/o͞o/ as in ooze	/oi/ as in oink	/ou/ as in ouch	/o͝o/ as in book	/aw/ as in awesome

CHALLENGING

1. should avoid the zookeeper's pet baboon (6)

2. went to the lookout point at Nassau Beach (8)

3. will play the kazoo while riding on a seesaw (9)

4. made a scrapbook about the flowers in my garden (9)

MORE CHALLENGING

5. gave me a goofy look during my awkward dismount (9)

6. want to sled downhill until four o'clock without pausing (9)

7. will learn to downshift into third gear in my dad's Toyota (11)

8. was disappointed with the brown sandalwood countertop (7)

CHALLENGING

1. "We have to pretend to enjoy Grandma's oyster stew," said Audrey. (11)

2. *The Austere Academy* is the fifth book in Lemony Snicket's book series. (12)

3. Shawna jotted down details about her Bigfoot encounter in her new, secret notebook. (13)

4. The groundhog chooses a spot near a new redwood tree each night to root for mushrooms. (16)

MORE CHALLENGING

5. I have an appointment for a booster shot, and I am feeling awfully brave this afternoon. (16)

6. Judy is counting all of her pennies and saving them up for the newest superhero comic book. (17)

7. Andrew Bradshaw put his chewing gum under the edge of the counter, and his little sister reported this to his mom. (21)

8. We have to try to get some autographs from the baseball players on the Detroit Tigers team while we are here. (21)

WORDS

1. Read each word.
2. Underline words with the /ōō/ sound.
3. Draw a box around words with the /aw/ sound.
4. Circle words with the /oi/ sound.
5. Double underline words with the /ou/ sound.
6. Draw a star (★) next to words with the /ŏŏ/ sound.

applaud	disappoint	magnitude
pronoun	footprint	soymilk
download	exclude	raccoon
sketchbook	surround	truthful
daunting	goodness	coward

CHALLENGE YOURSELF

1. Find the word that is a living creature. _____

2. Find the word that means "someone who is not brave."

   _____

3. Find the word that means "to clap." _____

4. Find the word that is something you can do on a computer.

   _____

Consonant Digraphs: two letters that work together to spell one sound

- There are six common consonant digraphs: ch, ck, sh, th, wh, ph

- Examples:

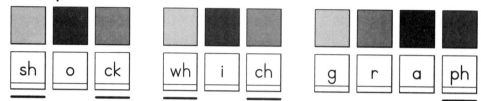

2-Sound Consonant Blends: two consonant letters next to each other that each spell a separate sound

- **Key info:** 2-sound blends can come at the beginning or end of a word.

  ○ *Beginning:* bl (bled), cl (clip), gl (glad), br (bran), dr (drip), gr (grip), fl (flip), fr (from), cr (cram), tr (trap)

  ○ *End:* ln (kiln), lk (milk), nk (rank), mp (ramp), nt (sent)

  ○ *Can be at beginning or end:* sk (skirt, mask), st (stir, last), sp (spill, gasp)

- Examples:

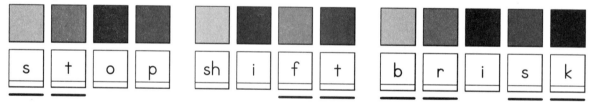

Digraph Blends: a 2-sound blend where a consonant letter spells one sound and a digraph spells the other sound

- **Key info:** Digraph blends can come at the beginning or end of a word.

- There are only a few digraph blends: shr, thr, nch, nth, lth, fth, lch, lph

- Examples:

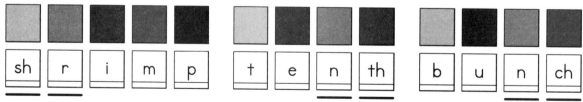

The letters qu: the letter **q** is almost always followed by the letter **u** `qu`

- Key info:
    - ○ In English words, the letter **q** is always followed by a **u**.
    - ○ The **qu** spells the sounds /kw/.
    - ○ The **u** in **qu** never acts as a vowel. It is part of the consonant spelling.
    - ○ The letters **squ** act like a digraph blend and spell the sounds /s/ /kw/.
- Examples:

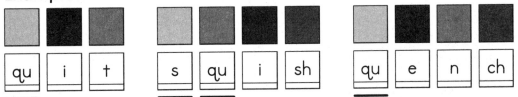

| qu | i | t |

| s | qu | i | sh |

| qu | e | n | ch |

Trigraphs: three letters that work together to spell one sound

- Key info:
    - ○ Trigraphs only occur at the end of words.
    - ○ The vowel sound before a trigraph is short.
- There are only two **common trigraphs:** tch, dge
- Examples:

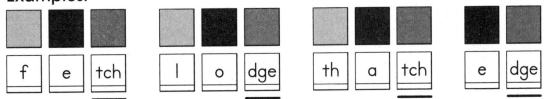

| f | e | tch |

| l | o | dge |

| th | a | tch |

| e | dge |

3-Sound Consonant Blends: three consonant letters next to each other that each spell a separate sound

- Key info: 3-sound blends can come at the beginning or end of a word.
- There are five common 3-sound blends:
    - ○ *Beginning:* str, scr, spr, spl
    - ○ *End:* mpt

▶ Glossary of Terms

- **Examples:**

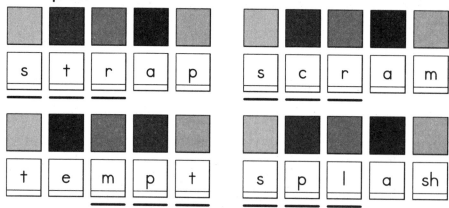

Letter y as a Vowel: the letter **y** is a consonant when it comes <u>before</u> a vowel letter (<u>y</u> e s). The letter **y** is a vowel when it comes <u>after</u> a vowel letter or <u>after</u> a consonant letter (b <u>oy</u>, sh <u>y</u>).

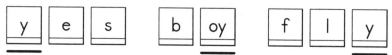

- **Key info:** The letter **y** as a vowel usually spells *long i* at the end of single-syllable words (my, shy, fly, try, by) or *long e* at the end of multisyllabic words (baby, lady, crunchy, cozy).

- **Examples:**

Schwa: /ə/

- is a "lazy" or "reduced" vowel sound because it has less energy than a typical vowel sound;

- is the most common phoneme in English;

- often occurs in multisyllabic words.

- **Key info:**

  - The most common sound for schwa is /uh/, like in zebr<u>a</u> and <u>a</u>void.

  - The other sound for schwa is /ih/, like in bask<u>e</u>t, lem<u>o</u>n, sal<u>a</u>d.

- Sometimes we need to "flex" a vowel sound to the schwa to pronounce the word correctly.

- **Common schwa spellings:**

    - *-on* (ribb<u>o</u>n, comm<u>o</u>n): the **o** in the ending **on** is often a schwa

    - *a-, -a* (<u>A</u>laska): **a** at the beginning or end of a multisyllabic word is often a schwa

    - *-et* (helm<u>e</u>t, bask<u>e</u>t): the **e** in the ending **et** is often a schwa

    - *-en* (sev<u>e</u>n, consist<u>e</u>nt): the **e** in an **en** is often a schwa

    - *-al* (dent<u>a</u>l, ov<u>a</u>l): the **a** in the ending **al** is often a schwa

    - *-le* (pebb<u>le</u>, app<u>le</u>): the **-le** ending contains a schwa plus the sound /l/

    - *con, com* (<u>co</u>nfess, <u>co</u>mmit): the **o** in the first syllable **con** or **com** is often a schwa

    - *-a-, -i-* (hex<u>a</u>gon, pres<u>i</u>dent, cat<u>a</u>strophic): the **a** or **i** in the middle of word is often a schwa

Syllable Types

Closed Syllables: syllables with only one vowel, followed by one or more consonants

- **Key info:** The vowel sound in a Closed Syllable is usually short.

- **Examples:**

    - *Single-syllable:*

    - *Multisyllabic:*

Open Syllables: syllables that end with only one vowel letter

- **Key info:** The vowel sound in an Open Syllable is usually long or schwa.

- **Examples:**
  - *Single-syllable:*

  - *Multisyllabic:*

Vowel-Consonant-e Syllables: syllables that end with a vowel letter, a consonant, and a final **e**

- **Key info:**
  - The VCE pattern is one of the most common ways to spell a long vowel sound.
  - VCE syllables often happen at the end of words.
- **Any vowel letter can be in a VCE Syllable:** a_e, e_e, i_e, o_e, u_e, y_e
- **Examples:**
  - *Single-syllable:*

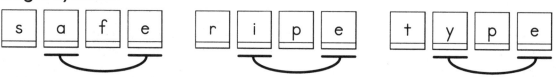

  - *Multisyllabic:*

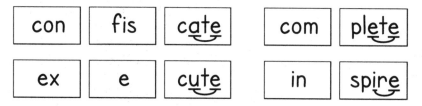

Vowel Team Syllables: syllables with two, three, or four letters that work together to spell one vowel sound

- **Key info:**
  - The vowel sound in a Vowel Team Syllable is usually long or other.
  - The letters in a vowel team stay together in one syllable.

- Examples of vowel teams spelling long vowel sounds:

| ai | ey | igh | oa |

- Examples of vowel teams spelling other vowel sounds:

| oo | ou | oi | aw |

- Examples:

| r̲e̲a̲ | son | | re | p̲a̲y̲ | ing | | nigh̲t̲ | mare |
| with | dr̲e̲w̲ | | en | j̲o̲y̲ | ment | | ap | pl̲a̲u̲d |

R-Controlled Syllables: syllables with a vowel letter or vowel team followed by the letter **r**, where the letters combine to spell an r-controlled vowel sound

- Key info:

  ○ R-controlled vowel spellings have two or three letters.

  ○ /ar/, /or/, and /er/ are r-controlled vowel sounds.

- Examples of r-controlled vowel spellings:

| ar | or | oor | er | ur | ir |

- Examples:

| t̲a̲r̲ | nish | | f̲o̲r̲ | giv | en | | b̲o̲a̲r̲d | room |
| e̲a̲r̲th | ly | | noc | t̲u̲r̲ | nal | | chi̲r̲p | ing |

Consonant-le Syllables: 3-letter syllables formed by a single consonant letter right before the letters **le**

- Key info:

  ○ Consonant-le syllables occur only at the end of multisyllabic words.

  ○ **-le** spells the sounds /uhl/ (schwa plus /l/).

- ○ **-le** acts like a magnet to pull the consonant before it into the final syllable.
- **Examples of consonant-le spellings:** -ble, -cle, -dle, -fle, -gle, -kle, -ple, -tle, -zle
- **Examples:**

| puz | <u>zle</u> | | star | <u>tle</u> | | cu | bi | <u>cle</u> |
| pud | <u>dle</u> | | bu | <u>gle</u> | | re | sem | <u>ble</u> |

Reading Multisyllabic Words

🐦 When reading longer words:

- Look for the vowel <u>letters</u>.
- Expand your vision to look for the vowel <u>spellings</u>.

🐦 First ask yourself:

- How many vowels do I see?
- Are they together or apart?

🐦 Then ask:

- Do I see a vowel-consonant-e?
- Do I see a vowel team?
- Do I see an r-controlled vowel?
- Do I see a consonant-le?
- Do I see a prefix, suffix, or any other familiar endings or chunks?

🐦 Finally, ask:

- How many vowel spellings are there?
- How many syllables will there be?

🐦 Remember:

- Digraphs always stay together, but blends can be split down the middle. (e<u>s</u>-<u>ta</u>b-<u>li</u>sh, qui<u>ck</u>-ly, co<u>m</u>-<u>p</u>lex)

- Doubled consonants are split down the middle. (**puz-zle**, **ap-proach**)
- When a vowel is by itself, not next to another vowel, it is usually the only vowel in the syllable. (**fan-tas-tic**, **Wis-con-sin**, **e-lec-tri-cal**)
- Vowel teams almost always stay together. (**sea-son**, **main-tain**, **a-stound-ing**)
- Vowels followed by an **r** almost always combine to spell an r-controlled vowel sound. (**bur-den**, **floor-board**, **for-bid-den**)
- Prefixes and suffixes are often syllables. They stay on one *SyllaBoard*™. (**dis-a-gree-ment**, **re-read**, **un-e-vent-ful**)
- If you see -**le** at the end of a word, it usually grabs the previous consonant and becomes a Consonant-le Syllable. (**jun-gle**, **pur-ple**, **fiz-zle**)

Common Vowel Spellings:

▶ Long a
Most common: a (Open Syllable), a_e, ay, ai

▶ Long e
Most common: e (Open Syllable), e_e, ee, ea, y

Less common: ie, ey

▶ Long i
Most common: i (Open Syllable), i_e, y, igh

Less common: y_e

▶ Long o
Most common: o (Open Syllable), o_e, oa, ow

▶ Long u
Most common: u (Open Syllable), u_e

▶ /or/ as in fork
Most common: or

Less common: our, ore, oor, oar

Glossary of Terms

/ar/ as in barn

Most common: ar

/er/ as in bird

Most common: er, ir, ur

Less common: ear, ar, or

/o͞o/ as in ooze

Most common: oo, u_e, ew, u

/ou/ as in ouch

Most common: ou, ow

/oi/ as in oink

Most common: oi, oy

/o͝o/ as in book

Most common: oo

Less common: u

/aw/ as in awesome

Most common: au, aw

Common Chunks

When you see one of these groups of letters in a word:

- Read them as one chunk that almost always spells the same sounds.
- Keep them together in the same syllable.

all	ang	ing	ong
ung	ank	ink	onk
unk	tion	sion	ture
cial	tial	cious	tious

Tracking Chart

Date										
Reader 1										
Reader 2										
Reader 3										
Accuracy % Goal: 98% or better	%	%	%	%	%	%	%	%	%	%
100%										
99%										
98%										
97%										
96%										
95%										
94%										
93%										
92%										
91%										
90% or below										
Words Correct per Minute (WCPM)										
140 or above										
135–139										
130–134										
125–129										
120–124										
115–119										
110–114										
105–109										
100–104										
95–99										
90–94										
85–89										
80–84										
75–79										
70–74										
65–69										
60–64										
55–59										
50–54										
45–49										
below 40										

WAY TO GO!

98% or better ACCURACY PERCENTAGE

▶ Tracking Chart

Date									
Reader 1									
Reader 2									
Reader 3									
Accuracy % Goal: 98% or better	%	%	%	%	%	%	%	%	%
100%									
99%									
98%									
97%									
96%									
95%									
94%									
93%									
92%									
91%									
90% or below									
Words Correct per Minute (WCPM)									
140 or above									
135–139									
130–134									
125–129									
120–124									
115–119									
110–114									
105–109									
100–104									
95–99									
90–94									
85–89									
80–84									
75–79									
70–74									
65–69									
60–64									
55–59									
50–54									
45–49									
below 40									

98% WAY TO GO! 98%